COME PONY TREKKING WITH ME

The Spencer family are looking for a holiday pastime for their children and decide to explore the possibilities of pony trekking. In this volume the reader can learn much about the ups and downs of such a venture from the experience of Carol and Hugh. They visit a trekking centre in Northumberland and then later progress to a larger one in Scotland, where Carol eventually decides to stay and make pony trekking her career.

The book should prove invaluable to young and old who are interested in holidays with ponies. The advantages and disadvantages of trekking are exploited and there is a stirring adventure with an errant rider and a thunderstorm.

In the final chapters the author discusses the day-by-day running of a pony trekking centre, including the schooling, feeding, shoeing and general care of the ponies.

COME
PONY TREKKING
WITH ME

Veronica Heath

Illustrated by Tom Carr

FREDERICK MULLER LIMITED
LONDON

FIRST PUBLISHED IN GREAT BRITAIN IN 1964 BY
FREDERICK MULLER LIMITED
PRINTED AND BOUND BY
COX AND WYMAN LTD. LONDON
FAKENHAM AND READING

CONTENTS

ILLUSTRATIONS

CHAPTER ONE

A MARVELLOUS IDEA

'Mummy, I've had a marvellous idea for a birthday present this year!' Carol Spencer came into the kitchen where her mother was preparing tea and threw her school satchel on to the draining-board. She was fifteen, tall and thin, but with an attractive, eager face and thick, dark hair which fell nearly to her shoulders. She pulled a stool out from under the table and crouched on to it. 'It's something I've been wanting to do again for ages and now there is a new place just started up . . .'

'Darling, do tell me what it is,' said her mother, picking up the satchel from the damp draining-board and placing it safely on a hook behind the kitchen door. 'We have been wondering what you would like and your birthday is only two weeks away.'

'I want to have riding lessons again.' Carol looked suddenly anxious as she glanced quickly at her mother. 'Jennifer Temple told me about this new place today, lots of the girls have been and the ponies are lovely and really it's not expensive. Oh, Mummy, please, don't look so glum . . .'

'Oh darling, I'm sorry, do I look glum?' Mrs. Spencer laughed and then picked up the bread-knife with a small sigh and began to cut slices from the loaf. 'But, Carol, what is it going to lead to?'

'What do you mean, Mum, why need it lead to any-thing?' Carol pulled a piece of crust from the back of the loaf and began biting it carefully like a rabbit with a lettuce leaf. 'It didn't lead to anything last time.'

'No, dear, it didn't,' Mrs. Spencer agreed. 'Because we simply couldn't afford to let it. That's what worries me. We have always known you would love to ride and have a pony of your own but it's quite impossible living here in in London even if we could afford to keep a horse, which we certainly can't.'

'I'm not asking you to keep a horse,' protested Carol, wrenching another piece of crust off the loaf. 'Just going and riding at this new place would be better than nothing.'

'For heaven's sake stop picking at the bread,' said her mother irritably, pushing two slices into the electric toaster. 'The point is, Carol, a few lessons wouldn't satisfy you. Naturally, you would want to ride more and get better at it and we wouldn't blame you.'

'Well, later on I could pay for it myself,' said Carol. 'That is, if I was any good, which I probably wouldn't be.'

'Yes, you would be, darling, I have always thought you would make a very good rider,' Mrs Spencer sighed as she looked at her daughter affectionately. 'You have just the figure for it and I know you love animals. It's a great pity for you and Hugh that we don't live in the country.'

'Well, we don't and it can't be helped,' replied her daughter sensibly, 'and it is no good wishing for what we can't have. Anyway, London has its good points,' she added, thinking about the Ballet her class had been taken to last week and the annual visit which her family paid to the glorious International Horse Show at the White City Stadium.

The front door banged and Mrs. Spencer looked up.

'Oh good, there's Hugh, he is early today,' she said. 'I'm afraid he doesn't take such a sensible view of London as you do, Carol.'

'Well, it makes him appreciate our holiday more,' answered Carol. 'I wonder what he would think about riding lessons, his birthday is at the end of the month too.'

The kitchen door was thrown open. 'Hullo, all!' Hugh burst in, his school cap perched on the back of a mop of fair, tousled hair and his blazer flapping open. He was two years younger than his sister, with a round, freckled face and blue eyes. 'What's this about riding lessons; there's nothing I'd like better for my birthday.'

'Oh, Hugh, don't tell me you want to ride as well,' Mrs. Spencer groaned.

'I don't just want to ride, Mum,' replied Hugh eagerly, letting his satchel slip to the floor and leaning over the table to his mother. 'I want to ride on our holiday this year too.'

'But, Hugh, don't be ridiculous.' Mrs. Spencer opened a drawer and pulled out a cloth impatiently. 'You know we are going to Grannie in Northumberland again.'

'No, Mummy, not this year,' broke in Carol. 'Daddy doesn't really want to –'

'Carol!' Mrs. Spencer stared at her daughter incredulously. 'Whatever next?'

'Well, what I mean is . . .' explained Carol hastily. 'He just said perhaps a change would be an idea this year and he thought of going somewhere near, where we could visit Grannie sometimes, but where he could do some fishing. You know he would love to, Mummy.'

'But, darling, whatever would Grannie think?'

'If she really thinks about it, Mummy, she would agree it was a jolly good idea,' replied Carol, getting up to help her mother spread the cloth on the table. 'You know last August she did get so tired with all those meals. Hugh's appetite was really disgusting!' She pushed her brother off the table on which he had perched himself.

'What about you!' retorted Hugh indignantly.

'No, but seriously, Mummy, I think Daddy is right,' went on Carol. 'Perhaps there is a nice hotel in Northumberland – or what about the Lake District – and Hugh and I could get some riding as well.'

Hugh nodded eagerly, his indignation forgotten. 'One of the chaps at school went on a riding holiday last year,' he told them, 'and he said it was absolutely super.'

'For heaven's sake, not so fast!' Mrs. Spencer pleaded. 'Hotels and fishing and now riding as well; I shall have to discuss this with Daddy before your imagination takes you any further.' She began rattling the cups and saucers down upon the table.

'But, Mum,' pursued Hugh, wanting to get a final word in on the subject. 'You must admit it is a good idea.'

'After all, Hugh and I aren't children any more,' sighed Carol, tossing her hair back and going to fetch the butter and jam from the cupboard. 'And apart from anything else it would be a much better holiday for you as well, Mummy. The last two years you have been slaving away helping Granny with the cooking and everything and there has been nearly as much work as you've had to do here.'

Mrs. Spencer paused. She thought momentarily of her mother, living alone in her beloved Northumberland, from where she had refused to budge when she had been widowed fifteen years ago. The annual visit from her only daughter and her family was the highlight of her year. But there was no doubt about it, each visit she found increasingly hard work and her only daily help was getting as old and slow as she was.

'Just think how you would enjoy a hotel, Mummy,' Hugh could see that his mother was tempted. 'All your meals ready for you and nothing to do at all, just go for walks or knit or whatever you want to do.'

Mrs. Spencer smiled at his eager face. 'Oh, darling, it

does sound tempting, doesn't it,' she agreed. 'And I suppose if you two are going to ride, you thought some riding lessons first would be a good idea?'

'Yes, that's right . . .' they both agreed enthusiastically.

'Well, we'll just have to ask Daddy,' she said. 'Goodness knows what he'll think about your choice of birthday presents this year. Now take off your blazer, Hugh, and go and wash your hands for tea, or you'll never get your homework done.'

To the children's great delight their father did not disapprove of their wish to have riding lessons. He thought that it would be healthy for them and good exercise. An excursion to visit the new riding school was arranged immediately and arrangements for them both to have lessons were made. Carol had ridden before and Hugh was an agile games player at school and his naturally good balance enabled him to learn quickly. He ignored the finer points of horsemanship, but after half a dozen lessons was beginning to rise to the trot and to demand that the leading rein be removed.

The question of the annual summer holiday inevitably arose again. Mr. Spencer was inclined to agree with the children about visiting a hotel.

'I think we can afford it this year,' he told his wife one evening as they drank their last cup of tea before going to bed. 'It would be a far better holiday for you than going to your mother. Granny will understand, she is much too sensible to take offence. I think she will probably be quite relieved really and we shall still see plenty of her.'

Mrs. Spencer nodded. 'Yes, dear,' she agreed. 'I've been thinking about it and have decided it would be a good idea and nice for you, too, if we can go somewhere where you can get a bit of sport.'

At the riding school

'I think I will write to The George at Ottershaws,' said Mr. Spencer. 'There's good fishing there and lovely walks and not too far from Granny's.'

'What about Carol and Hugh?' asked his wife, pouring herself another cup of tea and replacing the cosy carefully over the spout. 'They are so keen on this riding business that we shall have to go somewhere near a riding school.'

'No, Ruth,' Mr. Spencer shook his head. 'Not a riding school.' He paused and thoughtfully re-lit his pipe. 'I have been talking to one of my colleagues at the office. Reg Sinclair, you remember, the fellow with four daughters –'

Mrs. Spencer nodded and waited expectantly.

'Well, he seems to have hit on rather a good thing for

his family the last two years,' Mr. Spencer drew on his pipe reflectively. 'Apparently, over the last ten years there is quite a new type of riding started up which isn't terribly expensive and seems to have become a great holiday attraction. I think it might be the answer for our two youngsters this year.'

'For heaven's sake, hurry up and tell me more,' pleaded his wife impatiently. 'Those Sinclair girls are absolute tomboys so I can't imagine what you are going to suggest...'

'This new idea is called Pony Trekking,' replied Mr. Sinclair, who was not to be hurried. 'Apparently it appeals to adults just as much as children. In fact, Reg says some centres won't take children. Sounds a strange sort of sport, doesn't it, and yet, judging by bookings at various agencies, it is what the public want.'

'Pony trekking!' Mrs. Spencer retorted. 'Well, I don't know the back of the horse from the front but I don't think that sounds very exciting. How ridiculous for grown-up people to ride ponies. Absolute cruelty, I call it!' she looked at her husband to see if he was going to agree with her. To her surprise he did not reply immediately.

'No dear,' he said after a pause. 'I don't think it is so ridiculous. I have seen photographs of some of these treks and the "ponies" look quite big and everyone seems to be enjoying themselves very much. As a matter of fact,' he admitted, 'I have inquired at one or two agencies and there are some quite good places in Northumberland and Westmorland. I was hoping there might be somewhere the children could pony trek near Ottershaws.'

'Well, Tom, this certainly is a surprise,' said his wife. 'I had no idea you were even thinking about it. What about the children, have you discussed it with them?'

'No, of course I haven't, dear,' replied Mr. Spencer

'Personally, I think they will be game to try anything that is connected with horses and riding. But we shall see. Don't be too hasty in condemning the idea. I don't know what pony trekking entails any more than you do but I'm going to find out. I have a feeling it may be just what we are looking for this summer. And now cheer up, and let's have another cup of tea.'

Carol and Hugh were delighted to hear about the possibilities of pony trekking and thought it would be a grand way to explore Northumberland.

'The country around Ottershaws is lovely,' said Carol when they discussed the idea with their parents. 'But a lot of it is rough moorland. Perhaps that is why they use ponies in some districts now.'

'All the same I don't think I am very keen on a small pony,' said Hugh doubtfully.

'Perhaps they aren't so small,' replied his father. 'In the photographs they showed me at the agency, some of the ponies looked quite large.'

'Well, I hope so,' said Hugh. 'Anyway, I vote we ask Mr. Milne at the riding school when we go on Saturday. Perhaps he will have heard of "pony trekking" and can tell us more about it.'

'That's a good idea, Hugh,' replied his sister.

'Splendid!' agreed Mr. Spencer. 'I shall come with you. I'd be interested to hear what he has to say.'

Mr. Milne, at the new riding school, proved very helpful on the subject of pony trekking. He had never been on such a holiday himself but could tell them quite a lot about it.

'Pony trekking is a fairly recent recreation which has much to recommend it,' he told them. 'It particularly seems to appeal to townsfolk who have little experience of the countryside. Even complete novices, whatever their age, sex or size, can go pony trekking with perfect safety and confidence.'

'Goodness, do you mean that I could go pony trekking as well?' Mr. Spencer was astonished at this news.

'Of course, sir, if you've a mind to,' Mr. Milne assured him. 'No finer way to explore this old island. Much better climb a mountain sitting astride a hill pony, you know, than just admiring it from a car or a picture postcard.'

'Oh, certainly!' laughed Mr. Spencer. 'It sounds most exhilarating I must say. But surely you aren't going to suggest that I ride a pony up a mountain, not something like your pony, Topsy, over there ...' he indicated a small chestnut pony which was tied in the stableyard.

'No, sir, I wouldn't suggest that,' Mr. Milne assured him. 'The word "pony" is misleading for beginners. No adult would ride a pony as small as Topsy, she is 12.2 hands high.'

'How large is a "hand"?' inquired Hugh.

'Four inches is a "hand",' replied Mr. Milne, 'and only children at a trekking establishment would ride a pony smaller than that. Also, they are not allowed to use ponies under three years of age.'

Carol nodded agreement. 'That is the age when a pony is normally broken in, isn't it?'

'Yes, that's right, Carol,' agreed Mr. Milne. 'Their backs are not strong enough before that age to carry adults. But I must tell you about our native Mountain and Moorland breeds of ponies. These are the animals which are used in the best pony-trekking centres in the British Isles and I am sure you won't think it cruel to ride one of this type when you see how strong and agile they are. I have a book in my office which will tell you all about these ponies. I'll lend it to you, Mr. Spencer, and I am sure you will be interested.'

'Indeed, we shall.' Mr. Spencer thanked him grate-fully. 'As it happens I heard today from our hotel in Northumberland and they tell me there is a small trekking establishment quite near where the children will be able to ride.'

'That is splendid,' said Mr Milne. 'I hope they use Fell ponies. They are the native ponies of Northumberland and very fine ponies they are too, you will find out all about them from this little book.'

From the book which the riding school proprietor lent them the Spencers were able to learn all about the mountain and moorland ponies of Great Britain.

About fifty years ago herds of ponies ran wild in un-cultivated areas on Dartmoor, Exmoor, in the New Forests and in the Highlands of Scotland and the Fell country of Northumberland and Westmorland. From these districts the native ponies have taken their breed name. The herds usually consisted of about a dozen mare ponies belonging to different owners and headed by a stallion who ruled his family with a rod of iron. No mare was allowed to wander off on her own and if she did so she was promptly ordered back by the stallion. The little foals were born about May and almost at once showed extraordinary activity. For six months they led an idyllic life among the heather and bracken, trotting and cantering beside their mothers. In late autumn some of these herds of ponies would be rounded up and the six-month-old foals separated from their mothers and driven down to be sold at the nearest market. It was a terrifying experience for them and they were often sold for ridicu-lously low prices, even as little as £1 or less. Those young ponies who were fortunate went to private owners who recognized their sterling qualities and potentiality as children's riding ponies. Others were bought to work in the mines and, alas, there were many, particularly those which appeared small and stunted, who were sold to the slaughter-house for meat.

As time went on it began to dawn on horse lovers in England that these fine ponies would in time die out and were only being kept going by a handful of farmers. With all the potentially sound stock being sold for next to nothing the native breeds would soon be lost sight of if something were not done to save them before it was too late. Accordingly, the National Pony Society was formed and made great endeavours to get pony breed societies in the appropriate areas where the right type of mountain and moorland pony was being fostered. These societies took advantage of the National Pony Society's Stud Book for the registration of their ponies. In 1946 the National Pony Society distributed quite a large sum of money to the local breed societies with the idea that all the money should go to the maintenance of each of the breeds of their own true blood and type. It was expected that the district societies would do everything possible, in return, to work to the set type of pony of the district.

The genuine mountain and moorland pony had been proved to be a perfect mount for a child. Hardy, courageous and full of quality and character. Owing to the rough life he and his forebears had led he showed more brains than the horse. He had a great gift for dealing with difficult situations, crossing a stream, disentangling himself from wire or even escaping from a field. In the hunting field these ponies became well known for crawling or creeping through, or over, an obstacle if it proved beyond their powers to jump it. Many of them were well-shaped and narrow with astounding soundness and a hardiness which enabled their owners to keep them outside day and night in the roughest weather, provided they were properly fed.

B

The National Pony Society gradually grew from strength to strength. Today it is a flourishing concern and all serious breeders of our native ponies are members. The old aims of encouraging the right type of pony hold good as much now as ever they did, although pony breeding is being widely practised and our native breeds are not now in any danger of extinction.

The Shetland is the smallest breed of pony in the world. Although they are used extensively for riding and driving purposes in this country, and are very popular in the United States, it is difficult to see why they acquired their great reputation as children's ponies. Although many of them are quite suited to pulling a cart some are too broad in the back and neck to be suitable for riding purposes. Moreover some Shetlands are very naughty, however carefully broken, and they will buck and kick out of sheer devilment which is not what the parent requires for a beginner of tender years. Originally, these ponies did come from the Shetland Isles and lived a precarious existence there, finding their own support from the land, and occasionally some of their number being employed by the crofters to carry peat. They are remarkably strong and hardy for their size and generally stand between 9 and 11 hands high. They grow enormously thick heavy coats in winter and have luxurious manes and tails out of proportion to their stature. Black is a popular colour and ponies of this colour are reputed to be long lived and hardier, although this is a matter for conjecture. Dark brown, bay, piebald, skewbald and grey are also bred and the latter are particularly popular for pantomime and circus use.

Dartmoor ponies are slightly larger and stand up to 12.2 hands high. They are well-made, good-looking ponies, small and narrow with good heads and shoulders. They derive, as their name suggests, from Dartmoor and as is the case with all ponies born and bred on open moorland country, they have developed a strong constitution. Grey ponies are seldom seen, the usual colour being bay, brown, black or an occasional chestnut.

A pure-bred Exmoor pony can always be distinguished by its mealy nose, wide forehead, small pointed ears and large dark eyes. These ponies, like red deer, have always been on Exmoor and they have been heard of from early days being used as pack ponies. They are more true to type than most pony breeds because much care has been expended on them in the past by various pony enthusiasts. They are nearly always dark brown or bay in colour and should have no white markings.

Ponies from Wales can be divided into two groups, the Welsh Mountain ponies and the Welsh ponies of riding type. Welsh Mountain ponies are extensively used for driving but can be broken for riding as well. They pick up their knees very high when trotting and have a noble head carriage which makes them particularly attractive for harness work. The Welsh ponies bear strong resemblance to the Arab and are the most handsome of our native breeds and have roamed the Welsh hills for generations, the first records of them being as far back as 1138. The Mountain ponies must not exceed 12 hands in height and the riding type may reach 13.2 hands high. These ponies are not to be recommended for nervous riders as they are normally very keen strong ponies, admirable for showing and hunting, but not suitable for inexperienced beginners.

The Connemara pony comes from Ireland and twenty years ago the breed was hardly known to horse lovers. Since that time they have caught the public fancy and various breeding studs have now devoted themselves to the breed. They stand about 14 hands high and are nearly always grey in colour. The Connemara is generally good looking and they make excellent mares for show pony breeding purposes.

The last two breeds to be described are the true pony trekking breeds, the Fell and the Highland. They will carry an adult or a child which makes them an economic proposition for many families. The Fell pony originates from Cumberland and Westmorland and up to a hundred years ago they were used extensively for lead mining, each pony carrying about sixteen stones of lead ore in panniers on its back. In the northern countries many Fell ponies are still used by farmers and shepherds for rounding up their stock, for a large Fell pony can easily carry a man. They stand about 14 hands high and are thick-set and powerful. Walking is their best pace and they have a long free stride which enables them to trek for many miles over rough country without tiring. They are admirable at picking their way through bog and along stony hill-tracks. In colour the Fell pony is nearly always black, very dark brown or bay.

Highland ponies are sometimes known as Garrons in their native country and are still used all over Scotland for shooting, carrying stags or panniers of grouse according to the time of the year. They stand up to 14.2 hands high and are frequently dun in colour with a distinctive dark stripe down the back and on the legs. Grey and bay Highland ponies are also fairly common. They are tremendously strong ponies with good shoulders and feet and, like the Fell, are ideal for pony trekking purposes. A string of Highland ponies on a summer day, winding their way carefully up a hill-track through the heather, is becoming a common sight north of the border and a very attractive one it is too.

CHAPTER TWO

INTRODUCTION TO TREKKING

As the summer holidays drew near and the time for their initiation into pony trekking approached, the Spencer children began to gather together their riding equipment.

Carol had insisted upon having a pair of jodhpur boots. She was very proud of them the first time she went to the riding stables.

Mr. Milne duly admired them. 'Don't make the mistake of going pony trekking in them, though, will you?' he remarked.

'Why not?' Carol was dumbfounded. 'That's really what I got them for . . .'

'Oh dear, what a pity you didn't ask me about it first,' replied Mr. Milne. 'But I promise you they might become very hot and uncomfortable and strong shoes are much more sensible. You see, on trek there is sometimes the necessity for the rider to dismount and walk, and jodhpur boots are not ideal.'

'Oh bother.' Carol was very disappointed. 'I shall just have to wear them here after all. It is a good thing Hugh didn't get any too. Mummy has got him some second-hand breeches and he is going to wear them with his school stockings and shoes.'

'They will be fine,' Mr. Milne told her. 'Don't forget to take a small knapsack too. It might be useful to carry lunch in if you go out all day.'

'Good idea.' replied Carol. 'We hadn't thought of that. Do you think we shall need our Wellingtons?'

'Oh yes, certainly,' Mr. Milne replied. 'Although you may not use them if you are not able to help to look after the ponies yourselves.'

'Well, anyway, we wouldn't go away for a holiday without them,' Carol said, thinking of the wet days they had had on holiday the year before. 'By the way, I must get a new macintosh soon and Mummy doesn't want to buy me a proper riding mac; do you think I should have one?'

'No, not for pony trekking,' he replied. 'What you need is a lightweight macintosh, or a gaberdine which will roll up, if necessary, and fasten in front of your saddle. All the saddles will have small rings on the front and sides which are called D's and to which equipment can be fastened. I should avoid a plastic macintosh though, as they are inclined to tear easily.'

'Thank you so much,' Carol replied gratefully. 'What a good thing I asked your advice. Is there anything else you can suggest we should take?'

Mr. Milne considered the idea for a few minutes. 'You don't need a lot of expensive equipment to go pony trekking,' he told her. 'That is one of the attractions of the sport to the general non-horsy public. Some of the larger establishments send their prospective clients a list of suggested equipment too, which makes a useful guide for beginners. Oh yes, I can think of two very important items for you, a penknife and a length of strong string or cord. You never know when either is going to be needed on trek and they have a thousand uses.'

The drive north was always one of the best parts of the holiday for the Spencers. It was wonderful to feel that their holiday was just beginning and as the miles sped by and familiar landmarks were passed on the A1, the children grew increasingly excited at the prospect of two weeks' riding.

'I hope the stables are in the village,' said Hugh. 'Then we can help with the ponies every day.'

'I don't remember any stables in Ottershaws,' replied his father. 'But let's hope they aren't too far away.'

The pony-trekking establishment turned out to be nearly five miles from the hotel. This was a disappointing set-back and would necessitate the children being taken and fetched every day by car. Mr. Spencer felt it had been unwise not to have ascertained this beforehand because there was, in fact, a hotel a mile from the ponies. But the reservations had been made and they resolved to make the best of it.

'Will you take us over to the stables this morning, Daddy?' asked Carol as they sat at breakfast the first morning.

'Of course we will,' he promised. 'Your mother and I will enjoy a visit too.' Mr Spencer passed his cup to his wife for more coffee. 'I don't expect you will do much riding on the first day anyway.'

'This honey is just scrumptious,' said Hugh, helping himself generously to the delicious heather honey which had been provided on every table. 'Try some of it, Mum, I expect it comes from the moors around here.'

After breakfast they set out for the pony-trekking centre. The hotel manager had shown them the farm on a map. As they drove up the long stony lane to it they saw some ponies grazing in a field. They looked large heavy animals quite unlike the ponies in London. In the muddy stableyard, half a dozen other ponies were tethered. The Spencers felt rather dismayed and disappointed. Where were the stables and the grooms?

A young man came forward to greet them. He shook hands and told them that the 'operator' of the trekking centre, a Mrs. Nichol, had just gone to the field to fetch two more ponies in. He was apparently one of the farmer's sons who helped her with the ponies during busy

Ponies in the yard

holiday periods. Three other guests were in the yard looking very apprehensive. One of them, a young girl of about seventeen, clad in jeans and a brilliant purple jumper, confided to Carol that she had never been on a horse in her life before. Mrs. Nichol returned, leading two animals which, to the Spencers' inexperienced eyes, looked like small carthorses.

Mrs. Nichol introduced herself. She told them she was expecting three more visitors which would make the party eight altogether, and within a few minutes another car drove in and a family of father, mother and a large son of about fifteen stepped out in riding clothes.

The eight riders gathered around whilst Mrs. Nichol introduced them to each other and told them about the arrangements for the week's trekking.

'Today we shall have a preliminary talk,' she explained. 'This is essential for those of you who have never ridden before. After lunch we can ride in the field and find out which animal is going to suit each of you best and you will be able to stick to the same pony all the week if you wish.'

Five of the ponies were large black, handsome, animals with luxurious manes and tails. These animals were Fell ponies, the native breed of Northumberland. Mrs. Nichol spoke of them with pride and said that they came from a local stud where these fine ponies were bred. They were ideal for trekking work, she told her guests, and their ancestors had carried their owners over the hills for centuries. They were docile, sure-footed and wise and possessed an instinctive knowledge of the countryside. No Fell pony, for example, would willingly carry its un-suspecting rider through boggy or treacherous ground. The other ponies were cross-bred animals such as might be found in any riding stable, although none was under 13 hands high. They looked rough and muddy from the field but none of them appeared to be in poor condition and the saddles and bridles which the visitors would see laid out along the wall looked clean and well-kept.

Mr. and Mrs. Spencer decided to leave the children and promised to return for them at lunch-time. They drove away feeling rather disappointed at the turn of events.

'The children are soon going to get tired of ambling about on those animals,' sighed Mrs. Spencer. 'What a pity that the ponies are not even kept in proper stables. Such a dirty farmyard too . . .'

'Yes, I felt a bit disappointed as well,' admitted her husband. 'And such a nuisance that we shall have to fetch them back for lunch, we should have stayed at the hotel the other visitors are at; it was foolish of me not to inquire about the distance before.'

'Perhaps they will quickly get bored with pony trekking,' suggested Mrs. Spencer again, rather hopefully.

Back in the farmyard Carol and Hugh were far from bored. Mrs. Nichol was showing her guests the points of the horse and explaining to them how the pony was to be tethered when the riders were out on trek and the party stopped for a meal. A strong, safe, quick release knot was demonstrated to each rider by Mrs. Nichol and her assistant and they were told that each bridle was adapted so that the rope carried around the pony's neck whilst on trek could be fastened to the bridle and used for tethering. Carol and Hugh were very disappointed to hear that they were not expected to catch or groom the ponies. Mrs. Nichol told her guests with pride that they would be ready for them each morning when they arrived and that she did not expect any extra help after the rides.

'Will you tell us a little about the origin of pony trekking,' asked one of the guests.

Mrs. Nichol willingly agreed. She told them that 'trek' was a Cape-Dutch word originating from the Netherlanders and meaning to move off on a journey. In the old days it was measured by the speed of cape carts or ox wagons. In 1837 the Great Trek in Africa began when a party of Boers, becoming dissatisfied with British rule, gathered their families and flocks and set off in covered wagons to find a new country. Ultimately, these trekkers founded the Orange Free State and the Transvaal and were known as the Voortrekkers. Trekking in the British Isles has been operating for only about ten or fifteen years and is purely a holiday or recreational pastime. It had first been practised in the Highlands and seemed to catch the public fancy and proved an almost immediate success. There were now centres in Devon and Somerset, Cornwall, Northumberland, Westmorland, Cumberland and, of course, a large number in both the highlands and lowlands of Scotland and in Wales.

Trekking can be divided now into various forms of ride which should be explained to novices. Post trekking is beginning to be more widely arranged and involves the party of trekkers riding a distance and either staying at a convenient farmhouse or hotel, or camping out, and then continuing with the trek the next day. This goes on for several days, sometimes as long as a week, and is delightful for riders so long as the weather is not too inclement. Many miles of countryside can be travelled and the riders enjoy a unique experience. But many trekking centres cannot yet provide this form of amusement because of the extra expense and organization required and also because so many visitors are not experienced enough to be able to ride such long distances.

Day trekking is undertaken by all centres and means that the party leaves its headquarters early in the morning and proceeds for a distance of between ten or twenty-five miles, making a circular tour and stopping at midday for a packed lunch and a rest. Different routes are travelled each day and most of the trek is undertaken at walking pace.

Riding holidays are being arranged in many riding schools now and are more suited to adults and children who wish to progress at a faster pace than trekking can provide. More instruction in riding is given and there is generally a covered school or sheltered enclosed space where visitors can ride in all weathers. Instruction is also given in jumping and sometimes even in showing and hunting.

The morning was nearly over by the time Mrs. Nichol had finished talking and had demonstrated to the beginners the correct ways to mount and dismount and to hold

Ponies were allocated

the reins. Ponies were allocated to each of the eight riders and after lunch they proceeded very slowly in single file into one of the fields.

Carol was delighted to have been given one of the Fell ponies. A black mare with a luxurious mane and tail. She felt strangely heavy and broad when Carol first mounted her but after ten minutes on her back she felt certain that she had never sat upon such a comfortable pony. She responded pleasantly to the elementary aids that Carol was able to give her and broke quite willingly into a delightfully easy trot.

'I think we are going to be good friends, Bracken,' Carol told her pony, as she reined her in, after performing a figure of eight at the trot for Mrs. Nichol to judge how the two were suited to one another. 'I hope we shall be able to stay together.'

Hugh had been given a grey pony which he was finding rather heavy work. The pony shuffled rather unwillingly into a faster pace when he kicked it on.

'Keep your hands down!' Mrs. Nichol called out to him, 'and push him on with your heels. That's right, kick him on and shorten your reins; they are much too long...'

Hugh, very red in the face, began climbing up his reins and belabouring the lazy pony with his heels to the best of his ability. Mrs. Nichol could see that although he was very enthusiastic he had only been riding a short time.

'That is very good,' she told him encouragingly, when he rode over to where she stood watching. 'That pony is lazy and not easy for a beginner. I think perhaps I will take him and you can try one of the others.'

Hugh was then given one of the Fell ponies. He managed the pony easily and performed the simple tests that he was asked to do without mishap. The pony seemed very large after the small animals that he had been used to at the riding school and he rolled rather unsteadily in the saddle when they trotted.

'Blueberry is a reliable pony,' Mrs. Nichol told Hugh. 'You will soon get used to his action. He is used to children and he will take care of you. Ride over now to your sister and take the ponies around the field together.'

The children enjoyed the afternoon ambling about the field on the two Fell ponies and trotting and cantering

. . . Cantered in the field

when they felt inclined. It was pleasant to be free from the more organized atmosphere of the riding school.

'By the end of two weeks I shall feel that Bracken is nearly like my own pony,' said Carol, patting her mount affectionately as they rode back into the farmyard where their parents were waiting for them.

'That is what I always hope my visitors will feel,' replied Mrs. Nichol. 'These native ponies are very companionable animals and some of my clients have become very attached to them. I always try to let the visitors stick to the same pony for the duration of their holiday when possible.'

When everyone had dismounted and stretched their arms and legs and Mary and Violet and Nell, the three typists who were totally inexperienced, had voiced their relief at once more being on terra firma, Mr. Clements, the gentleman visitor who had brought his wife and son, asked Mrs. Nichol an interesting question.

'We noticed on your notepaper, Mrs. Nichol,' he said, 'that your trekking centre had been awarded the 'Ponies of Britain' Certificate for Approval. Could you explain what this means to us? We have had a rather unsatisfactory experience at another trekking establishment and felt that as you held a certificate, your place might be more promising.'

'Of course I will tell you all about it,' said Mrs. Nichol, 'and I'm sure what I have to say will interest everyone here. But first, Mr. Clements, will you tell us about your experience because I think it may help to illustrate what I have to say about our certificate of approval.'

Mr. Clements began to tell them a distressing tale. The previous summer he and his wife and son, who were all totally ignorant of matters to do with ponies and pony trekking, had visited an establishment which they had seen advertised in the press. It was being run by two young girls who appeared to be only sixteen, although they pretended to be older. The ponies were all thin and weedy and by the end of the week they could see that they were obviously not getting enough to eat. One pony was persistently lame but, because the girls were afraid to disappoint their clients, the animal was taken out every day. The girls kept their horses and ponies in stables which were never clean. Nine animals for two young girls to look after was obviously beyond their powers and the result was dirty stables and dirty ponies. The countryside was beautiful and the guests enjoyed the rides within limits. They felt unhappy about the animals they were given to ride.

'I am a big man,' Mr. Clements told them, 'and I felt uncomfortable all week riding the undersized animal that I was given, particularly as it looked thin. But there was not a horse in the stable that I could see was up to a man's weight or I should have seen that I got it.'

'Most of the ponies didn't have shoes,' said his wife. 'Surely, when there is roadwork, they should be shod?'

'Yes, of course they should,' replied Mrs. Nichol. 'A native pony which never had roadwork need not necessarily wear shoes but it doesn't sound as though any of these ponies were hill ponies.'

'Indeed, they were not,' replied Mr. Clements. 'None of them looked like these ponies here. Yet it was difficult for us to know what to do about the situation. To report the establishment to the R.S.P.C.A. would have been too drastic. They were nice girls and they did seem fond of their animals, otherwise they obviously would not have been working so hard at the job. But we were totally ignorant of the horse world and knew no one in authority to whom we might explain the situation. Yet surely, it was not right to use underfed and lame ponies?'

'We did pay quite a lot too,' interrupted his wife. 'Thirty shillings a day each we felt was expensive for the doubtful pleasure we enjoyed.'

'Yes, indeed,' agreed Mrs. Nichol. 'You certainly had an unpleasant experience. If you will tell me the name of the establishment I know who to report it to and will tell you about them in a minute. The girls will be helped and advised, which is obviously what they need.'

Mrs. Nichol began to tell her visitors about the work that was now being done for pony trekking in the British Isles. Scotland was one of the first countries to recognize the potentials of this type of holiday and the Scottish Council of Physical Recreation introduced it in 1952. They inspected and sponsored many centres and gave help as required, in order to keep up a good standard of management. It was obvious that the native Highland pony was ideal for the work and the Scottish Highlands can truly be said to have been the birthplace of modern pony trekking. Centres sprang up all over the country. Wales too, with its beautiful scenery, was an obvious choice for trekking holidays. After a while, reports began to spread of some establishments, such as the Clements had just described, which were not of a high standard. There was no recognized authority, except in Scotland, to whom the public could report these centres and in many cases they would have been unwilling to do so. Many people preferred simply to regard the holiday as a failure and did not choose to venture pony trekking again. Then in 1959 an organization called the Ponies of Britain Club, which had an expert knowledge of ponies, decided that something must be done to set a standard in trekking centres, so that the public and the ponies could no longer be exploited. A panel of judges were chosen by the Club and all trekking and riding holiday centres were invited to give these judges free access to their premises. All centres which

c

achieved the desired standard were to be awarded a Certificate of Approval.

Practically all the centres welcomed the inspectors and the majority were awarded certificates. These had to be renewed annually and a standard of 80 per cent efficiency had to be attained. The inspectors were extremely thorough and many of them went over each animal as carefully as a veterinary surgeon. In 1959, forty-five out of fifty-four establishments inspected, passed the test. Naturally, all sensible proprietors of trekking centres realized the worth of these certificates. The public now had something to go on and any establishment which advertised itself as an accredited Ponies of Britain centre was known to be of a certain standard.

'So you see now what our certificate means,' explained Mrs. Nichol. 'I open my doors to the inspector who comes to visit us very willingly.'

'Do they really send someone to inspect every year?' asked Carol.

'Yes, indeed, they do,' she replied. 'The Ponies of Britain Club is a workmanlike body and has done much for the pony world in Britain. Now I think it is time we turned these ponies out, they've all finished their feeds, and I will see you again at ten o'clock tomorrow.'

Everyone dispersed and the Spencers and the Clements drove away in their cars while the three secretaries, having declined a lift, set off to walk to their guest house.

'Did you ever see anything so funny as their clothes,' said Hugh as they passed the girls on the farm lane. 'One of them is wearing sandals, I could see her red toenails, fancy coming riding dressed like that!'

'Did you see their thin jeans?' added Carol. 'When they were riding the trouser leg worked up and their legs were quite bare against the stirrup leather. It must have been jolly uncomfortable.'

'I heard Mrs. Nichol talking to them about their clothes,' said Mrs. Spencer. 'She was very nice about it and of course, I don't see how girls like that would know any better. But it would have been much easier for them if they had been told beforehand what to bring. I thought they seemed so nice too and a jolly good holiday for them if they work in offices during the rest of the year. By the way, children, do you think you are going to enjoy yourselves – Daddy and I thought those ponies looked so heavy and slow . . .'

'Of course we are!' replied Hugh indignantly, 'and they aren't really as slow as they look. I only wish Mrs. Nichol would let us help her look after them.'

'Don't worry, Mummy, I think we are going to enjoy ourselves all right,' Carol assured her. 'I do agree with Hugh though about looking after them. Anyway, tomorrow we are going on a proper ride in the morning and next day I hope it will be a whole day trek.'

'I was very interested to hear what she had to say about this organization, the Ponies of Britain Club,' said Mr. Spencer. 'At first, Mummy and I felt rather disappointed that there were no stables and the ponies looked so rough. But perhaps for the country around here they are quite suitable and they certainly appeared to be well cared for.'

'What a ghastly experience that other family had,' said Carol. 'And such a waste of a holiday, I'm surprised that they ever thought of going pony trekking again.'

'Well, it might just as easily have been us,' replied her father. 'As it is we have made a very silly mistake not inquiring first about how far the hotel was from the trekking centre.'

Their route took them on to the main north road which was constantly busy at this time of the year with many holiday cars and caravans travelling up to the border. The

rolling Northumbrian moors were looking their best
with the purple August heather in bloom and as they drew
near Ottershaws the moors gave way to the large fields
which were grazed by the black-faced sheep of the
district.

CHAPTER THREE

PRELIMINARY INSTRUCTION AND FIRST TREK

'We are going to have a short lesson this morning and then our first ride,' Carol told her parents at breakfast the next day.

'Do you need a lesson, dear?' asked Mrs. Spencer in surprise.

'Yes, of course, Mummy,' replied her daughter. 'There is an awful lot about horses to be learnt, you know. Anyway, the three girls have never ridden before – or hardly at all, so they will have to be shown what to do.'

'I talked to Harry yesterday,' Hugh remarked. 'And he said we had to be shown the correct way to get on and off and –'

'Mount and dismount you mean,' interrupted Carol. 'And who on earth is Harry?'

'He is the man from the farm who helps Mrs. Nichol,' replied Hugh. 'He said she would show us the saddles and bridles and things, but, actually, I know all that.'

'What rot!' retorted Carol. 'I bet you don't know a snaffle from a curb – and don't eat all the toast, other people want some too.'

'It is quite all right, we can ask for more,' Mrs. Spencer assured her. 'What about this afternoon, darling, I think it is time you both came over and saw Granny, don't you?'

'Yes, Mum, this afternoon would be a good idea because there is no riding. Mrs. Nichol is getting some of the ponies shod. Anyway, we must see Granny and perhaps she will come over to the farm sometime.'

'Yes, I'm sure she will,' replied Mr. Spencer. 'And she will enjoy some days with us while you two are riding.'

'I hope you aren't going to get tired of those shaggy animals she has given you to ride,' sighed Mrs. Spencer.

'Oh, don't fuss about them, Mum!' said Hugh. 'We like them, don't we, Carol?'

'Yes, of course we do, I think they are going to be perfect for riding through the heather,' replied Carol. 'Do you mind if I go now, Daddy, I want to write a few postcards before we go to the farm?'

When they arrived at the trekking centre later in the morning the ponies were all tethered along a wall in the farmyard and Mrs. Nichol was waiting for her guests. The ponies had been groomed and fed.

'First of all I want to show you the saddles and bridles that we use,' she explained. 'Then you will be able to understand what each piece of equipment is for and why we have it. Then I shall instruct you in mounting and dismounting. Or, anyway, those of you that need it, and then we shall proceed on a ride. Now gather round Bracken while I show you her saddle . . .'

The riders clustered around the pony. Bracken had been standing resting a hindfoot and dozing quietly. She lifted her head and sighed gently, shaking her mane to dislodge the flies which buzzed about her ears. Carol went to stand by her head and stroked her neck under its heavy curtain of black hair.

'Git up, Bracken!' said Mrs. Nichol affectionately, and Bracken obediently stopped resting her hindleg and stood patiently while the saddle was placed on her back.

Mrs. Nichol explained that an ill-fitting saddle would

The quick release knot

not only be an uncomfortable seat for the rider but would quickly cause sores on a pony's back. If the pony flinched or shivered unduly when the saddle was placed on its back the reason probably was that the arch was too narrow and pinched the pony or it pressed too severely on the animal's spine. She explained that the front arch of the saddle should be wide enough to admit the hand on either side of the withers and should be quite clear of the spine.

'Will you tell us about sores and girth galls and what they are?' asked Carol.

'Yes, I will,' replied Mrs. Nichol. 'They can be such a wretched business in the trekking establishments and show only too clearly the wisdom of getting well-fitting saddles and of keeping them in good condition.'

'Does that really make any appreciable difference?' asked Mr. Clements. 'I mean keeping the saddles clean.

'It isn't so much keeping them clean,' explained Mrs. Nichol, 'as keeping the leather supple and soft by constant application of a good saddle soap. This applies to all the leather, bridles and halters as well. If they are neglected the leather soon becomes hard and cracked and buckles are difficult to fasten and in time straps will actually break. Sore backs and girth galls are often caused by a grass-fed pony, which has not been worked for a while and has become unduly fat, having its girths done up too tight. Or if a blanket has been placed under the saddle which in most cases is quite unnecessary, a fold will quickly produce a sore, particularly on an unfit animal. Girth galls generally occur in the elbow and should not be left until the skin breaks before being attended to or the pony is liable to be off work for many weeks before the wound heals. When a sore back or girth gall is seen to be developing the pony should be laid off work at once and a mixture obtained from the veterinary surgeon for applying to the affected part. You all know how uncomfortable you feel walking with a blister on your heel, well, that is how a pony feels when a girth gall or saddle sore has developed.'

'How beastly for them,' agreed Hugh. 'A blister can be agony.'

'Exactly!' laughed Mrs. Nichol. 'And so you see we do

Headstall and snaffle

what we can to prevent these troubles developing. Now pass me Bracken's bridle, Hugh, and I will show it to you.'

The bridle was a snaffle but it had been adapted in such a way that it was, in fact, a leather headstall with a snaffle bit, which was particularly suitable for trekking. A single rein was attached to the rings of the bit and a rope was attached to a small ring, called a D, under the pony's chin. This rope was to be used to tether the pony when striking camp.

'The snaffle bit is the most suitable for inexperienced

riders and I think the most suitable for the pony,' explained Mrs. Nichol. 'Anyway, animals used for trekking should not require severe bits and if they do they are probably not suitable for novices to ride on trek. A neck-strap is a very sensible idea,' and she indicated the strap which all the ponies wore around their necks, 'and most useful for the rider to hold on to, going up or downhill, or when the pony jumps a ditch.'

'What about martingales and double reins and curb chains and things?' asked Carol.

'Those things should not be necessary,' Mrs. Nichol replied. 'Certainly not for well-trained native ponies and the equipment in trekking establishments needs to be kept as simple and workmanlike as possible. Here, for instance, there are ten ponies and Harry and I do all the tack cleaning ourselves. Also, we get a large proportion of novices coming to ride and they could not manage two reins and more complicated equipment would mean much more lengthy instruction and a lot of visitors do not want that. If they do, they would be better to go on a more organized riding holiday.'

Mrs. Nichol next proceeded to show her guests how to mount and dismount. This, of course, was a very elementary lesson and was given primarily for the three girls who were the only complete novices. Carol had to demonstrate the correct procedure. With her back to Bracken's head she grasped the reins and the pommel of the saddle in her left hand and placed her left foot in the stirrup iron. Then, taking hold of the back of the saddle she pulled herself up until she could swing her leg over and lower herself into the saddle.

'Never let yourself come down into the saddle with a heavy bump,' explained Mrs. Nichol. 'Or the pony will soon learn to move away as soon as you begin to mount. Now, Carol, let's see you get off . . .'

Carol kicked her right foot free from the stirrup iron and began to swing it over the saddle. Mrs. Nichol checked her.

'Never dismount without first taking both feet out of the stirrups,' she told Carol. 'Your foot could easily be caught in the iron if the pony moved away and you would be left hopping after him with one foot on the ground and the other trapped in the stirrup. Also, do keep hold of the reins with your left hand when you get off. If the pony should move away, and some of the best trained ponies do sometimes, then you would be in another awkward position.'

When all the riders had mounted and dismounted the long-suffering Bracken, they each proceeded to their respective ponies and were installed in the saddles with the stirrup leathers adjusted to suit them. They were beginning to feel cold as the morning was overcast and cloudy and the ponies shook their manes and mouthed their bits impatiently whilst Mrs. Nichol lined everyone up in the yard.

'I like to see all my riders lined up in the yard for a quick inspection before we move off,' she explained. 'Don't get too near your next-door neighbour though. Harry go and sort those three out' – she indicated the three girls' ponies who were edging up against one another. 'Now when we are out on trek it is very important to keep a pony's length between yourself and the rider in front of you. These ponies will not kick but they will not like being crowded.'

The party began to move out of the stableyard. Mrs. Nichol led the way, with the three beginners immediately behind her and the others following. They took a track which led quickly out on to the moors. The farm was, in fact, largely moorland and sheep were the backbone of the district. As the party filed along the grassy track which wound through the heather they were able to admire the rolling Northumbrian moors which stretched almost as far as the eye could see. Here and there on the slope of a hill could be seen a tumbled collection of

The Northumberland moors

rocks and now and then a stunted pine or a few oak trees gave shelter along a burn. The heather was just beginning to fade and the purple blooms turning to orange and as the ponies brushed against them, the seeds rattled in their cases. Now and then a black-faced sheep lifted her head to stare as the procession passed, her prominent roman nose giving her face a stupid expression and her long coat trailing in a tangled matt about her.

The ponies followed one another quietly. Carol and Hugh had time to relax and look about them. Now and again Blueberry snatched idly at a piece of heather and

Hugh found the reins slipping through his fingers as the pony took him unawares. The wind was still blowing quite hard, which at least saved the ponies from the torment of the usual August flies, but necessitated the riders buttoning up their coat collars and hunching their shoulders against the cold. The party reached the brow of the first slope and Mrs. Nichol halted. As the riders came up they reined in their ponies and stood looking down into the dell below them.

The heather below them gave way to bracken growing all over the slopes of the hillside and interspersed with rocks and small boulders. About fifty yards down, the tree line began and the path disappeared into the oaks and the larch trees.

'There is a burn down there,' Mrs. Nichol pointed into the trees in the valley below. ' We will ride down and follow it along a short way and then make our way back to the farm. It is very exposed on the moors today and if it is going to rain we shall need shelter. It is not at all steep but if you feel insecure, try and grip with your knees, hold on to your neck-straps and lean back without pulling on the pony's mouth.'

The party began to descend. Mrs. Nichol continued to lead the procession and Mr. Clements brought up the rear. He had been told to call out if anyone appeared to need help. But the ponies were thoroughly accustomed to the work and proceeded slowly down the track one behind the other. Carol marvelled at how her pony picked her way, for their grass path had now become a stony one, covered with small flints and stones and rocks. She tried to grip the saddle flaps with her knees and held tightly to a lock of mane and the neck-strap and tried to lean back without pulling Bracken's mouth. She gave up trying to guide her as she was obviously much more capable of picking a way down than her rider.

Safely gathered amongst the trees at the burnside, the party settled themselves again in the saddle and Mrs.

... Was obviously more capable of picking a way down

Nichol helped them to gather the reins up again correctly. The three girls had lost their stirrups and these had to be restored and as it had begun to spot with rain, the macintoshes which Harry had rolled up and fastened in front of each saddle were now undone and put on.

They continued along the burnside, sheltered from the shower by the trees, but as they came out on to the moors again on their way back to the farm it was raining steadily. The ponies turned their heads away from the direction of the wind and hunched their quarters, quickening their pace to get away from the exposed track across the moor.

Back in the farmyard Mr. and Mrs. Spencer had come early to fetch the children. The rain was now pouring steadily down and Mrs. Spencer remarked ruefully to Mrs. Nichol that she hoped it was not the beginning of a wet week.

'My goodness, I hope not too,' she agreed. 'The country here is so beautiful in fine weather and it is miserable for trekking when it is really wet, particularly for the beginners.'

'Daddy, it's been a lovely ride,' called Hugh, jumping off Blueberry and shaking the rain from the brim of his velvet riding cap.

'Simply marvellous!' agreed Carol as she patted Bracken's wet neck and slipped to the ground. 'Daddy, you never saw anything so clever as Bracken coming down a stony path. She won't even let me show her the way, she's as clever as a cat!'

'So she should be,' replied Mrs. Nichol. 'These native ponies have lived amongst hills and moors for generations and trekking is what they were originally bred for.'

'Surely you are not going to put these ponies out in the field in this rain,' asked Mrs. Clements anxiously.

'But of course we are,' replied Mrs. Nichol. 'They have lived outside all their lives and are much healthier for it. They would only get chilled now if we shut them up, whereas if they go in the field they walk about and keep their circulation going. Actually, we are going to keep four of them in the stableyard now because the blacksmith is coming this afternoon.'

The party broke up and returned to their respective

hotels to change their wet garments and enjoy a welcome lunch.

'Tomorrow we are to take a packed lunch,' said Carol as they enjoyed the good food that the hotel provided. 'We are going on a trek towards Greenhead and Alwinton Lake. Mrs. Nichol said we should be at the lakeside by lunch-time.'

'Well, that certainly should be a lovely trip,' agreed her mother. 'Let's hope it is not as wet as it is today. Alwinton Lake is about four miles away, it is surprising how far those ponies seem able to travel'.

'Oh, that's nothing, Mum!' said Hugh. 'Mrs. Nichol said that by next week we should be doing twenty miles in one day if we want to.'

'Good heavens, darling, this is a holiday not an endurance test,' laughed Mrs. Spencer. But she was delighted to see that the children were still enthusiastic about their chosen holiday 'sport' despite the inauspicious set-up of the establishment and the inclement weather.

Next day was still cold but a strong wind kept the rain at bay and any threatening clouds on the move. Carol and Hugh, with the rest of their party, enjoyed a whole day trekking over the moors and through the woodlands, stopping now and again to admire the view or to examine a new plant or to watch an unusual bird. Perhaps a buzzard, hovering high above the heather, where he stayed poised whilst his keen eyes watched every move of his prey. Then, suddenly, he plunged downwards and swooped up the wretched tiny creature with merciless claws. Sometimes, along the chattering burnside a rabbit was to be seen, hunched for a minute in indecision as he twitched his ears to catch the sound of the ponies' hooves on the turf, and then catching a glimpse of the party he departed with a flash of his white scut down the nearest burrow or scuttled away into a sheltering clump of heather. Hares were fairly common, some as large as a small terrier and easily seen by the riders as they paused in a half-standing posture, fore-paws raised and ears twitching, before lolloping away with huge strides into the distance. The grouse in the area were few and far between but were a rare delight to the horseman when they did erupt with their hoarse distinctive cry 'G-back, G-back, G-back' from their haunts in the heather or from among a group of lichen-covered rocks. Roe deer lived in the forests of the area and hill foxes on the moorland but these were very rarely seen by trekking parties and generally only in the early evening. Small birds darted among the trees along the burnside and there was plenty for the keen bird-watcher to observe. Sometimes, a pair of golden plover could be watched, swooping and diving over a corner of the heather, and as the party approached they became frantic with their call 'ca-wee, ca-wee' as they feared for the safety of their fledglings tucked away in the heather below them.

When the trekkers reached Alwinton they halted for lunch and Mrs. Nichol instructed them all in the correct method of tethering their mounts.

'Sometimes when it is warm weather we remove the saddles from the ponies,' she said. 'But there is no need for that today and all we shall do is to loosen the girths.' She raised the flap of her pony's saddle after dismounting and let the two straps down two holes. Then she led the pony to a sheltering tree and using the rope which had been fastened around his neck, she tethered him firmly to the tree using the trekker's knot. Everyone was helped to do this and all the ponies were securely tied to their respective trees, well out of kicking range of one another, before the riders themselves began to explore their knapsacks and to settle themselves comfortably at the lakeside for a rest and some refreshment. Mrs. Nichol had told

D

them not to burden themselves with any unnecessary extras and to pack plastic drinking bottles, never glass ones, an extra jumper and their sandwiches, cake and fruit.

'I was hoping to bring my camera one day if it is fine enough,' remarked Mr. Clements. 'Do you think that would be sensible?'

'Perfectly all right so long as it is not too heavy,' Mrs. Nichol assured him. 'You want as light a camera as possible for pony trekking because on a hot day, and let's hope we get some, the knapsacks can feel very heavy by the end of the day.'

Carol and Hugh had brought their cameras too and were hoping for some fine weather to be able to use them. When they had finished their lunch they walked down to the lakeside and hunted for flat stones to skim over the water. The strong wind had at last blown the threatening clouds away and blue sky was beginning to break through. During the afternoon the sun shone fitfully as they proceeded over the moors back towards the farm.

Each day during their holiday at Ottershaws the Spencers enjoyed delightful treks over the Northumbrian moors and through the vast forest areas. Rides had been left through the new plantations which the Forestry Commission had planted extensively in the area, and provided the trekkers did no damage to the young trees and were careful to close all gates and to avoid starting fires, they were allowed to trek through these beautiful plantations. Some of the visitors preferred not to ride every day as there was a variety of other enjoyable pastimes to pursue in the area. The market town of Hexham with its golf course was near by and the beautiful northeast coast with the delightful seaside resorts of Holy Island, Bamburgh and Seahouses. From the latter harbour the Spencer children had enjoyed a wonderful day-trip to the Farne Islands the previous year.

As the time for their departure drew near Carol and Hugh were disconsolate.

'I shall hate leaving Bracken,' said Carol. 'She is a perfect pony for trekking. I only wish we could have done more to look after them. I should love to have groomed her and fed her and saddled up myself.'

'Me too!' agreed Hugh. 'And it's been a nuisance for Mum and Dad to have to keep fetching and carrying us from here to the hotel.'

They were riding home at the end of the last day's trekking. They fell behind the rest of the party to make the ride as long as possible. It had been a warm day and the children had removed their jackets and tied them around their waists. Their packs felt heavy although there was little in them.

'I wonder who will be riding them next week,' sighed Carol. 'Whilst we are back in London instead of here in this gorgeous place. Granny is lucky to live here, isn't she?'

'Yes, she certainly is,' agreed Hugh. 'But, Carol, what about next year. I'm sure Mum is wondering whether we've got this riding craze over, or not –'

'It is not a craze,' replied Carol. 'And I'm certainly not tired of it, far from it, in fact. You know, Hugh, I shall be leaving school next year and I'd adore to get a job in a place like this.'

'Gosh, Carol, you mean in a trekking centre!' Hugh was delighted at the idea. 'That would be wonderful,' he used the bracken frond that he carried to sweep a fly away from Blueberry's twitching black ears.

'The only thing is,' mused Carol. 'I would have to go to a bigger centre, somewhere with more ponies where they needed help. And I'm not qualified at all which is a pity, but perhaps that wouldn't matter because I have learnt a lot about riding in this last fortnight, and I shall go on riding at Mr. Milne's, if possible, all winter.'

'I can't imagine what Mummy will say when you tell her you want to work with ponies,' Hugh told his sister. 'I don't think she will be at all surprised to hear we want to go trekking again, in fact, I think they are expecting it.'

'Oh, I shan't say anything about getting a job in a trekking centre at the moment,' Carol assured him. 'There is plenty of time before next summer. So don't you say a word either, Hugh –' Carol broke off to shake her head irritably and to slap at her cheek. 'Ow – that was a midge, they always begin biting in the evening up here after a warm day.'

'Come on, let's trot!' said Hugh, who was beginning to feel the midges too. 'Here's a nice grassy bit and the others are well ahead so we won't upset them if we canter.'

They shortened their reins and urged their ponies on. Bracken and Blueberry quickened their stride and broke willingly into a trot. They tossed their heads to shake the flies away and snorted in pleasurable anticipation at the thought of their evening feed.

Carol stood in her stirrups and looked between her pony's neat pricked ears as they cantered over the short, mossy, turf. She grasped the reins in one hand and stroked Bracken's warm neck under the thick blanket of mane. 'Oh you are a beauty,' she sighed. 'I wish I could ride you every day in the year!'

CHAPTER FOUR

BACK AGAIN FOR ANOTHER HOLIDAY

'WELL, Carol, it seems clear to me that we must go into this pony-trekking business very carefully this year,' said Mr. Spencer. The family were settled in the drawing-room one wet Sunday afternoon the following spring. He leant back in his chair and drew reflectively on his pipe. 'We learnt a lot last year and there is obviously a wide choice of riding holidays. But if you are serious about wanting to work in one of these establishments then we shall have to make a number of inquiries.'

'If you really do want to get a job with horses why can't you work here in London at Mr. Milne's riding school?' suggested Mrs. Spencer hopefully. 'Then you could live at home.'

'No, Mum, it wouldn't be quite the same,' replied Carol patiently. 'It's the trekking I want to do and I love those native ponies they use. What I would really like to do is to go somewhere in the highlands of Scotland.'

'That would be very pleasant,' agreed her father. He sympathized with his daughter's choice of a job and could see the attraction in pony trekking. It would be a healthy happy life and if she did get tired of it in a year or two no harm would have been done.

'I'm leaving school in July,' said Carol. 'Perhaps Hugh and I could go to a trekking centre then for a holiday and

I could stay on and work there. I don't expect I would get paid, at least not at first, but I would be learning.'

'Yes, that sounds all right,' agreed her father. 'But what do these places do in the winter?'

'Most of them close down,' replied Carol. 'I asked Mrs. Nichol last summer and she said she turns her ponies out about November on the moor and then there is nothing to do but feed them every day. But she did say that some of the large centres are beginning to take working pupils. Pony trekking is apparently becoming so popular that the operators are going in for breeding from some of their best ponies while some of the young ponies are worked and trained during the winter by the staff.'

'What about going to Wales?' suggested Hugh, who was taking a keen interest in the discussion. 'We've never been there and I sho l think they would have some good places.'

'There is a Welsh Pony Trekking Association,' Carol told him. 'I found out all about where to write, from a girl at school. I've got lots of things to show you . . .' she got up and went to rummage in a drawer.

'Well, you are a dark horse,' said her father. 'You have obviously gone into all this pretty thoroughly already. I suppose you've landed a job on the quiet as well?'

'No, Daddy, not yet anyway,' laughed Carol. 'But look at this . . .' she showed them a pale cream booklet from the Ponies of Britain Club with a list in the back of all the centres in the British Isles which their judges approved.

Mr. Spencer glanced through it. 'What a splendid publication,' he said. 'Just exactly what the public need.'

'Then there is the Central Council of Physical Recreation in London and the Scottish Council of Physical Recreation in Edinburgh,' Carol read out to them. 'Lots of trekking centres are sponsored by them and regularly inspected. So I thought, if you agreed, that I would write to one or two of these recognized establishments in Scotland and offer my services. We could pay for a fortnight's trekking and then they might let me stay on and help and there would only be my board and lodging to pay for and after all there would be that in practically any job I chose to take.'

'Yes, of course,' agreed her father. 'That sounds like a sound suggestion, Carol. I don't mind paying for your board and lodging. I don't think Mummy and I will come with you on holiday this year, anyway.'

Mrs. Spencer nodded. 'You are both quite old enough to enjoy yourselves on your own,' she agreed. 'But Carol, must it be Scotland, it's such a long way away?'

'No, it needn't be Scotland, I suppose,' Carol replied. 'But I would love to go there. What do you think, Hugh?'

'Well, I must say the highlands do sound rather super,' he replied, enthusiastically. 'But I had been thinking about a proper riding holiday. This list of yours, Carol' – he indicated the brochure from the Ponies of Britain Club which he had been studying – 'says that some of the riding schools are residential and you can get in some jumping and visits to shows and things. That sounds rather fun!'

Carol made a wry face. 'Oh, Hugh,' she said, 'I don't want to work in a riding school, I want to go to a trekking centre. And the Highland ponies that they use in Scotland look so gorgeous . . .'

'Oh, all right, I don't really mind,' Hugh agreed. 'After all, if you are going to stay and work at the place I suppose it ought to be your choice.'

'Well, if you have set your heart on the highlands,' said Mr. Spencer. 'You seem to have a fairly wide choice here. Let's pick out one or two likely establishments and write to them.'

The response was encouraging but it was clear that most of the centres to which Carol wrote were already well-staffed and were very particular about letting guests trek with untrained instructors. She would have to work hard at learning about ponies and conducting treks before she could expect to go out alone with a party. But two of the centres were willing to accept her as an unpaid helper for six months or more, if she seemed promising during the fortnight's holiday.

'Well, that seems to me very fair,' said Mr. Spencer as they studied the letters together. 'I particularly like the sound of this place in the Cairngorms, and you might be able to enjoy some ski-ing if you are still there in the winter. Mrs. Cameron of the Croftmore Trekking Centre. It is a lovely part of the highlands; I have been to Rothiemurcus which is quite near.'

Carol was thrilled. It was lovely to feel that her parents were in agreement with her choice of a job and she wrote to Mrs. Cameron at once to say that she and Hugh would be travelling up to spend a fortnight with her as soon as their school broke up for the summer holidays. The rates for each of them with board and lodging and the use of a pony each was fifteen guineas. It seemed quite reasonable when the cost of keeping a pony all through the year had to be taken into consideration.

'After all they can only be hired for the summer months,' explained Carol. 'Then the operator has to keep them all winter. And they look lovely ponies from her brochure.'

'Last year we paid twenty-five shillings for your day-trekking in Northumberland,' replied her father. 'So I don't think fifteen guineas all in is too bad. She promises a certain amount of instruction too and you should be able to feel that the ponies are really yours for the two weeks. After that I am afraid it may be very hard work and not so much fun. You will have to help the other guests and not expect so much riding for yourself.'

'I don't mind that,' Carol replied. 'It will be gorgeous just to be working with the ponies.'

Mrs. Cameron sent all her prospective trekkers a list of suggested equipment. This was very helpful and already the Spencers had a certain amount of gear from the previous year. But if they wished to take part in any post-trekking there were further necessities that the centre advised.

'Gosh, Carol, post-trekking that sounds wonderful!' said Hugh as they studied the brochure together. 'It means sleeping under canvas, doesn't it?'

'No, I don't think it always means that,' she told him. 'In the remote districts like the highlands I think the riders stay at different farmhouses and ride on during the day. But I suppose a lot depends on the weather. Anyway, it doesn't say we have to bring a tent.'

'But it does say to bring a sleeping-bag,' pointed out her brother. 'Also a knapsack which we've got – but we shall have to get another one.'

'It says here that a pocket-knife with an attachment for taking stones out of pony's hooves is useful. That sounds a good idea. I think I shall certainly get one of those for myself,' said Carol.

'Oh bother, I haven't any pocket-money left,' wailed Hugh.

'Ask Daddy, he'll probably get you one if you tell him it's on the list, or you can borrow mine,' said his sister.

Carol had to equip herself for what she hoped would be a long stay. She already had a hard velvet cap, a tweed jacket and some jodhpurs and the jodhpur boots, but a new macintosh was going to be essential. It was decided to buy a short riding mac on the advice of the expert in a well-known riding and hunting clothes shop in London.

Jeans were packed for stable work and several head scarves and thick jerseys.

'I had better take a few skirts and a dress or two,' Carol said to her mother. 'It says in the brochure that evening parties are sometimes arranged, so Hugh had better take his best school suit.'

'Whoopee!' shouted Hugh. 'I can hardly wait to get there . . .'

There was not much longer to wait. The children caught the train to Scotland early the next morning. It was to be a long journey taking the whole day and necessitating two changes. When they reached Edinburgh during the afternoon they felt that they were really over the Border. There was no time to leave the station and explore the town before catching their connexion to Aviemore which was their destination, but they enjoyed this last long stretch of their journey most of all.

The new Forth road bridge at the Queensferry was a wonderful sight and they had a perfect view of the magnificent structure as their train roared over the immense railway bridge which had already spanned the Forth for nearly a hundred years. After this, the country became more attractive the farther north they travelled. Perth, Pitlochry and Killiecrankie were all well-known names even to Carol and Hugh who had never visited Scotland before. There was then a long stretch with rolling hills and heather and only clusters of cottages to be seen around the small stations. Newtonmore was a place which Carol knew was connected with pony trekking, and judging by the mountains and forests which they could still just see in the half light from the train window it looked a perfect setting for riding.

When the train at last steamed into Aviemore it was dark and the children were thankful that their long journey was over at last. They quickly secured their baggage and jumped down on to the platform. Mr. Cameron had come to meet them. He was a cheerful rugged-looking man who shook them warmly by the hand and bade them welcome. Then he took them out to his Land-Rover and stowed their suitcases in the back.

'Jump in!' he told them, 'and we shall soon have you both at the farm. It's a long way you've come from London but I'm sure you will think our corner of the highlands worth it when you see the Cairngorms in the morning. We've had some rare weather too, even for July, so let's hope it will last into the new month for you.'

'We have looked forward so much to coming,' Carol told him. 'And I'm so looking forward to meeting Mrs. Cameron and seeing your ponies. Have you been busy with trekkers this summer?'

'How many ponies have you?' inquired Hugh eagerly.

'To answer your sister first,' said Mr. Cameron. 'Yes, we have been very busy and we are full up at the moment. My wife is in need of your help when your holiday is over. Now, to deal with your question, Hugh, we have about thirty ponies at the moment, of which twenty are in regular daily use for trekking.'

'Gosh, thirty ponies!' Hugh was thrilled. 'There certainly will be plenty for Carol to do. What about the other ten which are not being used for trekking?'

'Well, they are mostly young stock,' replied Mr. Cameron. 'We have two mares with foals and several yearlings and two-year-olds. Then there are three young ponies which my wife has partly broken already and she is going to work on them this winter with the idea that they will be ready for trekking next year.'

The headlights of the Land-Rover lit up the pine trees which grew close to either side of the road. As they drove through a small village the notice 'Rothiemurcus' was lit by the car beam for a second, and a little farther on Mr. Cameron slowed the Land-Rover to cross a small bridge.

'This is the Croftmore Bridge,' he told them. 'It is our nearest shop. Our route takes us a little way up the Glenmore road now. I expect you will have heard about Glenmore, it is a National Park and has now become famous also for ski-ing. Now we turn up here to our farm.' They swung off the tarmac road which led to Glenmore and began to bump along a stony farm track.

Mrs. Cameron came out of the farmhouse to greet them. It was quite dark and the children could see nothing of their surroundings and so they stumbled willingly into the small hall of the house. Mrs. Cameron was dressed in a kilt and a green jersey. Her warm welcome and easy manner made them forget their momentary shyness at arriving and put them quickly at ease. She took them up the narrow farmhouse staircase.

'We have several guests sleeping in two small bothies,' she told them, 'but as I hope Carol is going to be a permanency I have been able to accommodate you both in the house. I expect you would like a meal now and a bath and then bed, but before you turn in I will show you the dining-room where we all breakfast at eight-thirty, and the visitors' lounge.'

The next morning Carol woke early. She wondered for a moment what it was that had woken her. Then she heard it again right outside her window. A cock was crowing lustily. She looked at her watch and saw that it was only six-thirty. She slipped out of bed for a moment to look out of the window. As she had a back room there was little to be seen but a sloping field partly covered in bracken and two black cows waiting at a gate chewing the cud. Her feet felt the icy cold lino and she hopped quickly back into bed and hunched herself under the bedclothes. She would have to wait another hour at least before she could possibly get up.

About seven-thirty the house began to stir and she heard voices in the passage and then heavy shoes clattering downstairs. She got up and dressed and when she was nearly ready Hugh came into her room.

'The others have got up and gone to catch their ponies,' he told her enviously. 'I can see them from my room. I suppose we will do that every morning before breakfast.'

'Yes, I expect we can start tomorrow,' agreed Carol. 'Come on, Hugh, let's go and watch them.'

They went downstairs and out of the front door. There was a small porch in which the visitors kept their macintoshes, shooting-sticks and knapsacks. The immense vista of the Cairngorm mountains took the children's breath away for a moment. The hills rose immensely high. Immediately below the small garden several fields surrounded the farm and in these they could see ponies grazing. Beyond the fields the purple heather line began and surrounded the croft.

The trekkers were bringing their ponies into the yard. Mrs. Cameron led the way and called out a greeting when she saw Carol and Hugh standing outside the farmhouse. They went over and joined the party eagerly.

The farm buildings were built round a cobbled square and what had obviously once been cow byres, had been converted into stalls for the ponies. A small byre had been left for the two house cows but the Camerons chiefly concentrated on sheep now because the land was not rich and the trekking business was proving a good sideline to the farm.

The Highland ponies were similar in build to the Northumbrian Fell ponies which Carol and Hugh had met the year before. They were mostly dun or cream chestnut in colour, with distinctive black points, and many of them had a dark stripe down the middle of their backs. There were also several greys. Each pony was led into its stall and then the temporary 'owners', each in charge of a pony for the duration of their holiday, went to queue at the fodder shed with their pony buckets where Mr. Cameron measured out the animals' rations.

Mrs. Cameron took Carol and Hugh amongst the ponies and told them a little about each pony and what they were called. The animals stood with small ears cocked in anticipation and nickered a welcome when their breakfast arrived, nudging the bucket and snorting hungrily. Their coats gleamed and their luxurious long manes and tails looked clean and well brushed.

'After we have had our own breakfast we always spend twenty minutes grooming our ponies before saddling up,' explained Mr. Cameron when Carol admired the ponies' appearance. 'I will give you both a lesson this morning. Now, Carol, I think you have met them all, except the young stock which we don't bring in each day, and so now we will go and meet the two ponies which I have allocated to you and your brother.'

Hugh's pony was a grey mare about 13.2 hands high. 'Is she a Highland pony?' he asked.

'Yes, she is indeed!' Mrs. Cameron assured him. 'She is a pure bred Highlander. Some of my best garrons have been greys. She is a real hill pony and she will take you anywhere, Hugh.'

'What is her name?' asked Hugh. He patted the pony who nudged eagerly at him, expecting her feed. She was a very light grey in colour, almost white, and despite her small size compared to some of the other ponies her round quarters looked strong and powerful.

'Her name is Jean,' replied Mrs. Cameron. 'I have had her many years and she has given me two foals. One of

'Is she a highland pony?'

them is now a three-year-old and should be in full work by next season.'

Carol had been making friends with her pony. Another mare, larger than Jean and a pale creamy dun in colour with a shaggy mane and tail. She had the large, kindly, dark eye of the pure Highlander, the distinctive black stripe down her back and her delicate velvety nostrils were also black. She nibbled at Carol's jacket and blew politely to tell her to hurry up and bring her breakfast.

'You're a lovely pony,' said Carol, as she stroked the pony's neck.

'Yes, isn't she a beauty?' agreed Mrs. Cameron proudly. 'She is from a very fine strain of Western Island ponies which I obtained some years ago. Her name is Dene Beauty Belle, but we call her Belle for short, and I broke her for riding myself. I think next season I shall breed a foal from her but I have several more exactly like her which I purchased at the same time. Now bring their buckets and come to the fodder house where Angus will give you the ponies' rations.'

After the children had enjoyed their own breakfast, and a very fine one it was of porridge and scrambled egg, they went out to the ponies to groom them before the day's riding. In a small wooden box under each pony's manger the children discovered their grooming kit. A dandy brush, a hoof pick and a rubber curry comb.

'Now then, roll up your sleeves,' directed Mrs. Cameron, who looked very workmanlike herself in a khaki overall with the sleeves rolled up. 'And if you prefer to do your grooming work in jeans to save your jodhpurs getting too dirty there will always be time for you to change before we leave for our ride at ten-thirty. Jodhpurs are ideal for riding but they can be very uncomfortable and hot to work in.'

Mrs. Cameron showed the children how to brush their ponies all over with the dandy brush to remove any dried mud or sweat which may have been left from the previous day's riding.

'Start at your pony's head and work down the neck and chest with long strokes. Don't dab at the pony with the brush. Work all over his body, cleaning his legs as well.' Mrs. Cameron was working on Jean's sides with Hugh's dandy brush as she spoke. 'Remove any sweat crystals around the girth area most particularly because if they are neglected they can easily cause girth galls and sores.'

Having groomed both sides of the pony, Mrs. Cameron then demonstrated how the feet must be cleaned out with

Instructions on Grooming

E

the hoof pick. No water was to be used on or in the hoof or on the hair around the pony's pastern because water can get into the hollow of the heel and cause cracks and sores. To pick up the pony's off forefoot she stood by Jean's shoulder facing her tail. Running her right hand down the forearm she grasped the leg above the knee. Then she pushed with her elbow until Jean shifted her weight on to her other foreleg at which Mrs. Cameron slipped her hand farther down and grasped the fetlock, which is the long hair that grows around the pastern. 'Come up!' she commanded and Jean obediently lifted her foot and had the small stones and dirt which had collected during the night carefully picked out.

'Surely she will kick when you try to pick up a hind-leg?' asked Hugh, watching the procedure with great interest. 'Or do we just leave the hind feet?'

'No, indeed we don't,' replied Mrs. Cameron. 'It is quite easy. These ponies are handled like this every day and are quite used to it.' She stood against Jean's flank facing her tail and ran her hand down to just above the hock. Grasping the fetlock with the other hand she lifted the hind hoof quite easily. 'Always stand close against your pony's quarters when you do this,' she told them. 'Then she couldn't kick you if she wanted to. Beginners often make the mistake of standing too far away and making nervous grabs at the leg – then the pony might possibly kick. She will wonder what you are up to!'

After this, the mane and tail had to be well brushed with the dandy brush. The mane and tail can add greatly to the general appearance of the pony, especially when they are as luxuriant as those of the native ponies, and the comb must never be used for this job. The brush is used with a complete downward movement, passing the whole length of the tail before being lifted. If the job is done regularly tangles will not develop.

'The curry comb is only used on the pony when it is very muddy,' Mrs. Cameron explained. 'But it is very useful for cleaning the brush . . .' and she showed the children how to do this.

When all the ponies had been groomed to their rider's satisfaction the order to saddle up was given. Carol had a fairly good idea how to do this from watching, and sometimes helping, at the riding school in London, but she wisely pretended ignorance and prepared to listen to her instructor.

The saddle was carefully lifted on to the pony's back. It was placed high on the withers and then pushed into its natural position on the pony's back. This ensures that the hair is lying smoothly under the saddle. The girth is drawn up carefully, and not roughly or jerkily, so that the pony learns that he will not get pinched and has nothing to fear. The bridle is taken in the left hand and the pony approached from the left-hand side. The rider stands against the pony's head and the rein is slipped around the animal's neck before the halter is removed. Then, should the pony draw away when the halter is taken off, he is securely held by the reins. When the halter has been removed the rider holds the top of the bridle with the right hand and the bit in the left. The bit is pushed into the pony's mouth. As soon as the pony takes it, the bridle is pulled over the ears and the mouthpiece will fit exactly into the animal's mouth. The throatlash is done up quite loosely.

'You will soon get used to doing this yourselves,' Mrs. Cameron told them. 'Most of my visitors pick it up very quickly. But Angus and I are always in the stables to help anyone who is in any difficulty.'

The ponies looked very fine, all clean and saddled up waiting for the ride. They stood mouthing their bits and snorting gently through their nostrils in anticipation.

Some of the riders departed into the farmhouse to change or to collect macintoshes which were rolled up and fastened in front of their saddles. With twenty pony trekkers, quite a number of them complete beginners, Carol could see that Mr. and Mrs. Cameron were kept very busy.

'You will have to learn what to do,' remarked Hugh to Carol as they stood holding their ponies in the yard prior to mounting. 'After your holiday you will be teaching them.' He indicated the groups of trekkers who were bringing their mounts into the yard, calling out for assistance with a mac which refused to roll up or a stirrup leather which was too long, or a pony which would not stand to allow them to mount.

'No, I shan't be teaching them,' replied Carol. 'I haven't learnt enough myself yet to be an instructor. But I'll be helping and I can see that there is going to be plenty to do!'

CHAPTER FIVE

MORE USEFUL INSTRUCTION

THE trek was divided into two groups of ten riders. Mrs. Cameron took the beginners and her husband led the more experienced riders.

'I would like you and your brother to come with me this morning,' she told the children. 'I have never seen either of you ride and I must have an idea of your capabilities before I allow you to trek with Angus. He takes his riders over much hillier country than I do.'

The trekkers departed in single file down the rough stony track which led away from the farm and through the pine trees. Silver birches grew in profusion in the area and everywhere lichen-covered rocks and stones littered the ground. When the party reached the farm boundary the party divided, Mr. Cameron to lead his riders up the glen to the north of the farm and Mrs. Cameron to head for Loch Moran.

'We shall trek to the head of the loch,' said Mrs. Cameron, 'and eat our lunch at the far end before we return this afternoon along the opposite shore.'

The ponies stepped out willingly and even the complete beginners in the party were able to manage the steady walking pace.

'Lazy ponies are more trouble than they are worth,' Mrs. Cameron told Carol, noting with appreciation as she did so, that the girl was riding her pony with good balance and confidence. 'I think it pays to feed the animals well each day when they are in full work. Any pony worked straight off grass is going to be slow and unresponsive. Hard work necessitates hard food.'

'But do you find beginners can manage fit ponies?' asked Carol.

'Much better than they would lazy ones,' replied Mrs. Cameron. 'These ponies are used to trekking in single file, that is what we school them to do when they are young. They are seldom over-fresh or naughty. But when they drag behind and need kicking on all the time or snatch at the grass, then they really are a nuisance. Inexperienced riders are not strong enough to correct them and the party is continually being held up. I like to lead the trek and where possible to take individual riders alongside for instruction, but if the ponies behave badly I have to bring up the rear so that I can see what is going on.'

Loch Moran was set in a beautiful valley with pine trees growing along one shore, right down to the edge of the stony beach, and the heathery slopes of a hill bounding its other side. Their way led them through the pines first, about a mile along the edge of the loch. As they rode Carol noticed the abundant wild life of the area. Delightful red squirrels raced up pines when they spotted the riders coming through the trees and small birds darted among the branches. The ponies picked their way cleverly over the places in the forest path where the roots of a tree sprawled across their way or rocks and stones were scattered about. The sun had come out and the loch looked a deep, mysterious blue. Carol wondered how deep it actually was. She had read that some of the Scottish lochs were as deep as the hills around them were high, which was a staggering thought. Across the loch the heather rolled away into the peaks of the Cairngorm range and Carol could see that here was a wealth of glorious riding country for trekkers to explore. They could ride every day for a week and never cover the same ground twice.

At the head of the loch the party halted. Mrs. Cameron dismounted and everyone was instructed to do the same.

'Put your reins over the pommel of your saddles and behind the stirrup leathers,' she told her party, at the same time showing them how this was done. 'Then loosen your girths by two holes.' She lifted her saddle flap and holding it up with her head she loosened her pony's girth. Two riders followed her example without taking the precaution of keeping hold of their ponies while they did so, with the result that the ponies began to walk away. This was put right and the tricky art of holding the pony in the left hand whilst loosening the girth with the right was demonstrated.

'Now we shall lead them down to the loch for a drink,' said Mrs. Cameron. 'Keep a pony's distance apart, there is plenty of room for them all here and just take them to the edge, there is no need to get your feet wet.'

When each pony had been watered they were tethered firmly to trees at the edge of the forest. They rubbed their heads against the trunks of their respective trees enjoying a satisfying scratch, or browsed quietly in the welcome shade. A few nibbled at the heather which struggled up sparsely amongst the roots of the trees.

The riders now unpacked their lunch packs, and leaving the forest moved a little way away from the ponies out into the open heather before settling themselves to enjoy the welcome fare. The ponies attracted flies and it was pleasant to be free from this irritation whilst they ate.

'Will we see any stags?' asked Hugh looking at the vast panorama of the hills to the east of them as he munched his sandwiches.

'We might not see any stags,' replied Mrs. Cameron.

. . . Down to the loch for a drink

'But possibly some hinds, which are the female deer, when we trek higher up.'

'Don't they live among the trees as well or always in the hills?'

'At this time of year, especially in fine weather, they are generally on the high tops,' explained Mrs. Cameron. 'In bad weather they often come down to the tree line especially in the evening. The end of September and October is the time of the rut and then I have often seen a travelling stag down here at the head of the loch where we are now. They love the peat hags and there are lots about here among the heather and they roll in them to cool themselves. These, of course, are red deer, quite large animals about the size of a small pony. Then living in the woods are the roe deer. These are the red deer's smaller relations, very attractive diminutive creatures but very timid and shy. There are quite a large number of them in Rothiemurcus forest now and I expect we shall see a few during our rides.'

Carol had finished her lunch. She looked across to where Belle, her Highland pony, was tethered to her tree. She was dozing in the shade with her head nodding slightly. Her bottom lip drooped and she rested a hind-leg. Now and again she twitched an ear to dislodge a fly which crawled irritatingly.

Carol stretched herself full length in the heather. The wiry stems scratched her hands as she lay with them under her head and she could hear a bee buzzing importantly from one heather bloom to the next. Above her the blue sky dazzled her eyes as she watched the small white clouds moving slowly along. What a glorious place this is, she thought, and how far from the noise and dirt and bustle of the big city which was their home. She wondered how her parents were and knew that they would be missing them very much. She resolved to write a long letter describing their doings and the beauties of the district. Hugh would never rise to more than a post-card. Lovely country to explore, good ponies to ride and pleasant companionship, what more could they ask? She would tell her parents that they had made a perfect choice.

'Come on, Carol, wake up!' Hugh came and threw himself down beside his sister.

'I wasn't asleep!' retorted Carol indignantly as she

roused herself with an effort and closed her eyes again for a moment to shut out the brilliant glare of the sky.

'I think we shall be starting back soon,' Hugh told her. 'Mrs Cameron is checking the ponies' girths now.'

Carol stood up and brushed some ants from her jodhpurs. 'Isn't this a super place, Hugh?' she said.

'Marvellous,' he agreed. 'I had no idea Scotland was such a grand country. I think you're jolly lucky to be staying on here, Carol.'

Carol nodded. 'Yes, it's going to be lovely but I don't know yet whether I shall be all right. But I can see that they need an assistant.'

They walked over to their ponies and after drawing up their girths, they untied the tethering ropes and fastened them around the ponies' necks. They fastened their sacks on the D's on the saddles and slipped the stirrup irons down the leathers. Then they led their ponies out into the heather and mounted, settling themselves in the saddles whilst the ponies stood quietly, swishing their tails and mouthing their bits.

The trek home during the afternoon took the party along the opposite shore of the loch. It was very hot and Carol rode in her short-sleeved aertex shirt. Her arms burned from the sun and she knew she must get some suntan lotion if the glorious weather was going to last. The ponies' fat sides gleamed with sweat although it was too warm to do more than walk. When they entered the pine trees again the welcome shade was refreshing and quite soon they reached a river which had to be forded. The ponies entered the water eagerly, lowering their heads to blow on the water and enjoying the coolness on their legs and feet.

Mrs. Cameron called out a warning. 'Keep your ponies' heads up and kick them on at once if they begin to paw the water.'

Several ponies had stopped now and were taking a drink. Mrs. Cameron had taken up a position in the middle of the stream to see her trekkers safely through. She held her pony's head up firmly on a tight rein.

'She has finished drinking now, Hugh,' she told him. 'Don't let Jean linger but push her on at once.'

Fording the river

The party struggled through one after the other. Carol's feet were splashed but she had managed to keep her pony going and they scrambled safely up the muddy slope on the other side. When they were all over Mrs. Cameron explained her caution.

'You must always keep your pony moving when fording a river,' she told the trekkers. 'Don't deny them a drink but beware as soon as they begin to paw the water. The pony probably wants a bathe when he does that, especially on a hot day like this.'

Someone laughed at this suggestion. 'What a good idea!' he said. 'Couldn't we let them have a soak?'

'It does sound refreshing,' Mrs. Cameron agreed. 'But you see they won't wait until you get off, which you certainly wouldn't want to do in the middle of the river anyway, and you could easily be rolled on and I can assure you it would be very unpleasant.'

Everyone saw the wisdom of this. It would certainly be disconcerting if the pony was to go down underneath its rider.

'I had one pony who was a devil for water,' Mrs. Cameron told them. 'She was a splendid trekking mare in other respects. I always had to take her myself if our way took us through water. She would be down on her knees in the river in no time if she wasn't kept going.'

They continued on their journey and at about four o'clock saw the signpost to Croftmore farm. It was still warm and pleasant but the midges were beginning to bite.

'It's been a lovely day, Mrs. Cameron,' said Carol riding alongside her on a wide stretch of the path. 'I haven't enjoyed myself so much for ages.'

'I'm so glad,' Mrs. Cameron replied. 'Of course the weather isn't always so perfect, alas, far from it sometimes. But the country here is always delightful in which ever direction we go.'

'I think it is beautiful,' said Carol. 'And Belle is a lovely pony.'

'Next week we are going to arrange a tour – or "post trek" – for some of our riders,' Mrs. Cameron told her. 'And I think if you and your brother would like to, it would be all right for you to join the group.'

This sounded wonderful. Carol was eager to know

more. Apparently the trek was to take them over the hills for several days, the nights to be spent in various farmhouses *en route*.

'We find sleeping under canvas is a lot more work,' explained Mrs. Cameron. 'It can be very difficult if the weather is bad. But we had a tour on these lines earlier in the season and it was a great success despite bad weather. There will be no trekking here during the four days that we shall be away so that Angus and I can both go.'

'It sounds super.' Carol was thrilled. 'How many riders do you take?'

'We have seven booked for the tour,' replied Mrs. Cameron. 'Then there are yourselves which makes nine and Angus and me. We could take twelve of us if anyone else seems competent enough to come. But you will find the riding tiring, Carol, so don't miss a day's trekking before next week, except Sunday, of course, when the ponies and ourselves have a day off. You will need to get fit.'

'I certainly won't miss any,' promised Carol. 'I couldn't bear to, I have enjoyed today so much.'

When they reached the stables and dismounted, Carol found that she was indeed very tired. It had been a long day in the saddle. Hugh stretched himself wearily when he slid off Jean.

'My legs feel quite stiff and aching,' he said, stamping on the cobbled yard. 'And, gosh, am I hungry!'

They led their ponies into their stalls in the improvised byres. Mr. and Mrs. Cameron hurried round everywhere, helping trekkers to unsaddle and easing the work of watering and feeding.

First of all the saddles and bridles had to be removed and the ponies tethered with their halters. It was important to lay the saddle down correctly on its fore-end on the ground so that the cantle was not damaged.

Then the ponies had to be rubbed down with a wisp of hay. This was made quite easily from a handful of hay about two feet long which was rolled into a coil and tied in an ordinary knot. This was then used on the pony, particularly along the back, under the saddle, round the line of the girth and behind the ears. The wisp, like the dandy brush, was drawn along the way the hair grows except where the animal was very damp and sweaty when it was necessary to rub hard to dry the area.

When the ponies had been rubbed dry it was necessary to water and feed them. Each pony received a good ration of concentrates or pony cubes and then the tired trekkers made their way into the house to enjoy tea and a short rest.

After tea and a change into comfortable clothes everyone proceeded into the stable yard for tack cleaning. As it was a fine evening they were able to do this outside. Hooks had been put in all along the wall and there were several buckets of warm water for washing the leather.

Mrs. Cameron brought her own tack over to where the Spencers were waiting. They were standing looking doubtfully at the bucket of water, the sponges and the chamois leather with which they had been provided.

Hugh scratched his head and sighed. 'I wish we had thought of asking Mr. Milne to teach us about all this before we came,' he said.

'Don't worry, you'll soon learn,' Mrs. Cameron told him. 'Come and help me drag another saddle horse out of the harness-room and I'll give you both a lesson.'

The saddle horse was a wooden construction on which two or three saddles could be placed for cleaning. The stirrup leathers and girths were stripped off and the stirrup irons placed in the bucket of water for the dirt to soak off. Then the saddle and the stirrup leathers were washed with the sponge not too wet and dried with the wash leather.

'Never dry wet tack near a fire,' Mrs. Cameron told her pupils. 'This will harden it too much and cause it to crack.' She slipped away for a moment to help another group who were struggling with their bridle buckles. Carol and Hugh carefully washed their saddles, paying particular attention to the inside flaps and the girth straps as they had been instructed.

The next step when the leather had been dried was to apply saddle soap. This was provided for the riders in large tins and special sponges were used. 'Don't use the sponge which you have just washed the leather with,' explained Mrs. Cameron. 'And you must rub the saddle soap well in, don't merely dab it on the leather.'

The girths were nearly all made of webbing and these had to be brushed clean when the mud from the ride was dry on them. 'In time they do become stained,' said Mrs. Cameron, 'so we scrub them about every two or three weeks. It is not practical to wash them every day because they take a long time to dry. Some girths are made of leather and these are cleaned with saddle soap like the rest of the leather. But I do not have many leather girths because I find they are more likely to cause girth galls.'

'They are beastly things, aren't they?' remarked Carol, remembering what Mrs. Nichol had told them about girth galls and saddle sores the previous year.

'Oh, they are the scourge of the trekking establishments,' agreed Mrs. Cameron. 'At least the dirty, badly run centres suffer very much from those troubles. Some ponies suffer with warbles too and no matter how careful you are it is not always possible to avoid them.'

'Warbles?'

'What on earth are they?'

Carol and Hugh had never heard of this pest.

'They are hard lumps which appear on the ponies' backs in spring and early summer. They are the maggots of the warble fly which has laid its eggs during the previous summer. If the warble is situated under the saddle it is likely to cause trouble because its maturity is hastened by the warmth of the saddle, so as soon as one is discovered in that area the saddle must be kept off.'

'What a nuisance,' exclaimed Carol. 'That means you can't use the pony for trekking?'

'That's right,' agreed Mrs. Cameron. 'But, of course, we treat them immediately they are detected. When the warble maggot, which is the lump, has ripened, we squeeze the base of the warble with both thumbs and the maggot pops out—'

'How horrid!' Carol was disgusted.

'Yes, they are horrid,' Mrs. Cameron laughed. 'But we have to treat them with respect. It is important not to exercise pressure with the thumbs before the warble is ripe or there is danger of bursting the maggot under the skin.'

'What happens when the maggot has been got out successfully?' asked Carol. 'Surely the sore place still needs to heal.'

'Yes, that's right,' replied Mrs. Cameron. 'We dress the cavity with diluted T.C.P. or sulphanilamide powder. The healing process should only take a few days but even that time lost with a good pony at the height of the trekking season can be most annoying.'

They had finished their saddles, the stirrup irons had been removed from the water and dried and replaced on the leather. The brushed girths were laid neatly over the

saddles. Next, the bridles were hung up on a hook and all
buckles unfastened. The bit and leather parts were all
washed, dried and then well soaped before the parts were
reassembled.

'It will take you a few days to remember where each
piece goes,' Mrs. Cameron told her pupils. 'But it is
surprising how easy it is when you are used to fitting the
pieces of puzzle together. Look, this brow band is on
back to front, Hugh . . .'

She adjusted his bridle. 'Be sure to soap your reins well.
I am very particular always to get narrow reins for my
ponies, it is so difficult for novices to manage thick ones.
They need to be kept soft and pliable with regular care
and attention.'

'What about polishing the bits?' asked Carol. 'At the
riding school in London I have sometimes seen them use
Brasso.'

'Yes, that used to be necessary,' agreed Mrs. Cameron,
'because most of the bits and irons and curb chains were
made of steel. But now it is possible to buy all these
things in rustless steel so it is not necessary to do more
than remove the dirt and grease by washing and polishing
with a dry cloth. It really pays to keep your pony's tack
in good condition by regular and careful cleaning. This
will make it last for years, and as good saddlery is expensive this is very important.'

Carol resolved to heed this piece of advice very carefully if she should ever have the pleasure of owning a
pony of her own.

Sponges and wash leathers were wrung dry and put
away and the saddle horses carried back into the harness-
room. Beside each stall the pony's respective saddle and
bridle were kept. The final job was to turn the ponies out
in the paddocks to graze for the night.

In single file the trekkers proceeded out of the yard

leading their ponies. Belle seemed anxious to reach her field and when Carol took her through the gate and pulled the headcollar over her ears, she shook her head with delight at her freedom and trotted away, swishing her tail at the midges. In the middle of the field she paused and then suddenly sank down on to her knees on the grass.

'What on earth is Belle doing?' Hugh was astonished.

'I think she's going to roll,' replied Carol. 'Yes, look, some of the other ponies are doing it too!'

'Gosh, don't they look funny!'

The ponies' legs had folded underneath them and they were now rolling luxuriously from side to side. Some of the heavier ponies were very slow, lying on one side for a few minutes before heaving themselves over again. They enjoyed the tickling sensation of the short grass on their skins and they rubbed their necks up and down on the soil with pleasure.

'Getting nice and dirty again for us to clean in the morning!' remarked one trekker.

When each pony had rolled to his satisfaction he heaved himself on to his legs again and shook himself. Then, after surveying his companions for a second, he wandered away, cropping the grass here and there until he found a tasty spot at which to settle for a while.

The days at the Croftmore Trekking Centre passed quickly. Much too quickly for Carol and Hugh who were enjoying every moment of their holiday. The days were very full, with looking after their ponies, and trekking all day, and sometimes dancing or enjoying informal parties in the evenings. There were a number of hotels and guest houses in Aviemore and neighbouring villages and Mr. Cameron would take a number of his guests to any party or festivity which was being held within a reasonable distance of the farm.

If they preferred to spend the evening at the farm there was a comfortable lounge in which to read and relax. Carol took advantage of Mrs. Cameron's library of horsemastership books and studied some of these with a view to improving her knowledge of ponies.

Sunday was a day of rest at the centre for ponies and riders. Some of the visitors who had cars went off for the day, others enjoyed walks or some fishing in a local loch. Carol and Hugh helped Mr. and Mrs. Cameron to feed all the ponies and then spent a happy day exploring the immediate neighbourhood. The wild life was a delight to them and there was plenty to see if the rambler trod carefully through the pine trees and the silver birches. August was a particularly good month to admire the fungi which are a feature of the highlands. Hugh discovered several splendid specimens of the common inky toadstool and in shady moist places they found the elegant little broom fork-moss.

The children trod carefully and quietly so that they could watch the red squirrels which seemed to abound in the district. They are much rarer and much more attractive than their grey relatives. The squirrels were cheeky characters and let the children get quite close sometimes. They would skip across the deer track in front of them and scramble half-way up the nearest pine tree. Then they would pause and poke their heads around the trunk and with their sharp little pointed ears cocked and their bright shoe-button eyes shining they waited to see what was going to happen next. When Hugh got too close they disappeared in a flash with a flourish of their bushy tails, or retreated higher up their tree to wait and watch again.

Ant heaps were everywhere in the forest. Sometimes

Hugh could not resist taking a stick and poking it into a heap, some of which were astonishingly large. The result of this investigation was a devastation to the hordes of ants who swarmed furiously over the end of the offending stick and all over the gaping wound in their house.

'It's cruel to do that, Hugh,' Carol told her brother. 'Just think how long it has taken those tiny ants to build these heaps.'

'Yes, I know it is,' agreed Hugh, poking the stick even deeper into the hole he had made. 'But I can't resist doing it now and again. Carol, just look at all those millions of pine needles the ants have used, it must have taken months to build such big heaps.'

'Years, I should think, so stop spoiling all their hard work,' replied Carol. 'Look they're crawling over your shoes now so it serves you right.'

Hugh threw his stick away through the trees and brushed the furious little ants off his shoes. 'I wish we could see some deer,' he said.

'You make too much noise,' said his sister. 'They say there are quite a lot of roe deer around here so we ought to see some if you wouldn't keep talking.'

'Well, I like that!' Hugh was very indignant. 'It was me who saw those rabbits in that old quarry first.'

'They heard you though, because they were on the run when we saw them. All we saw were their white tails –'

'"Scuts" you mean!' Hugh corrected her.

'Good heavens, is that their proper name ?' asked Carol.

'Yes, I was reading a nature book from the shelf in the lounge last night and it said so in that,' replied Hugh. 'Oh, look, Carol we're coming out on to the moor again. Let's go home by the ruined cottage we passed on the ponies the other day.'

'Righto!' Carol agreed. 'But we shall have to hurry, we don't want to miss tea.'

They began to walk fast along the narrow sheep track through the heather, enjoying the keen highland wind which ruffled their hair and the panorama of heather and hills which stretched as far as the eye could see.

CHAPTER SIX

THE POST TREK

THE next day was spent preparing for the post trek which was to start out the following morning. The party was to spend three nights away from the centre and this meant that a certain amount of equipment had to be carried. Arrangements had been made to accommodate the trekkers at different farmhouses *en route* and for rations of oats and bran to be available for feeding the ponies. This would eliminate a great deal of carrying of heavy fodder.

'We shall take one pony as a pack horse,' Mrs. Cameron told the party as they groomed their mounts during the morning. 'There are still only eleven of us going and they can manage twelve ponies. So we will take Prince to carry some of our equipment.'

'Gosh, just like a real trek!' exclaimed Hugh.

'Well, it is a real trek,' laughed Mrs. Cameron. 'Just wait till you see the route we have planned for you. We really are going up into the hills ...'

'How super!' Carol was laboriously brushing Belle's tail. 'I hope we aren't caught out in a storm or anything.'

'I sincerely hope not,' replied Mrs. Cameron. 'But it is very unlikely at this time of year. Anyway, we always take the precaution of leaving exact details of our route with our cook, Mrs. McNab, here at headquarters. Then if we don't turn up at our destinations each evening they can get in touch with her and she will know where they would be likely to find us.'

Careful attention was paid to each pony's feet before embarking on the trip. It was important that no shoes were loose and that all feet were in hard condition.

'It would be infuriating to loose a shoe during our journey,' said Mrs. Cameron. 'Even a loose one could be troublesome.'

'How long do the ponies shoes last?' asked Carol.

'About six to eight weeks,' replied Mrs. Cameron. 'But it depends upon the amount of work the animal is getting and whether it is doing much roadwork. Some ponies use the same shoes all through the season, but they are in the minority.'

'I noticed that your young ponies which are not being used have no shoes on,' said Carol.

'Oh no, we never shoe ponies which are out at grass,' Mrs. Cameron replied. 'Apart from the unnecessary expense there is the danger of them causing damage to one another by kicking. Shoes are removed from all the ponies at the end of the season when they are turned out. But we do need to watch their hooves and keep them regularly pared during the winter according to growth and to prevent them splitting.'

They were carefully taught the correct way to fasten their packs on the saddle. It was important that they should be firm enough not to work loose and correctly placed so that there was not undue weight on the pony's back and loins. The pack pony, Prince, was going to be very useful because for such a large party there was a fair amount of stuff to be carried. Not very much in the way of rations, except chocolate, apples and similar extras but each trekker had a complete change of clothes, a sleeping-bag, a macintosh, washing things and personal necessities. it was surprising what seemed to be needed for only three nights away from headquarters.

'What an awful lot you must need to carry when you

take a party out to sleep under canvas,' said Carol. 'Tons of stuff I should think. I mean, tents even . . .'

Mrs. Cameron laughed. 'Well, not tons of stuff, thank goodness!'

'The tents are the lightest of the burden,' Mr. Cameron told her. He had been passing with a barrow load of stable manure on his way to the midden. He laid the barrow to rest a minute and straightened his back. 'We take light cotton tents. No, Carol, the rations for the party are the heaviest item. Food for ourselves and the ponies.'

'Yes, I can imagine the pony's food would be a burden because it is so bulky. Surely, they can feed on the grass and heather?'

'Yes, during the night they can. But you couldn't possibly expect a pony to travel fifteen or twenty miles on nothing but grass.'

'Of course not.' Carol remembered what Mrs. Cameron had told her about the ponies requiring hard food for hard work. 'But for the riders you would need a kettle and a pan and cutlery and mugs . . .'

'And, of course, the food!' broke in Hugh.

'Yes, all those things and more,' Mr. Cameron nodded. 'But if you learn to pack methodically it is amazing what a party can carry without too much inconvenience. Particularly, when they have a pack pony to go along too. Oh well,' he sighed and bent to pick up the barrow again. 'Standing gossiping here is not going to get the work done.'

During lunch, which they had in the farmhouse that day, it began to rain. As it was a steady drenching rain and there was no wind at all which might have helped to drive the wet away the ride which had been scheduled for the afternoon was cancelled. There was no point in ponies and riders getting drenched when they were going out on a long trek the very next morning. Some of the guests departed in cars for the afternoon and others remained indoors. Carol and Hugh obtained permission to spend the afternoon with Jean and Belle, preparing them for the next day. They had already been groomed during the morning but now they were brushed all over again.

'I don't expect we shall be cleaning tack regularly for the next few days,' said Carol, carefully brushing out Belle's tail. 'So we had better give it an extra "do" this afternoon.'

Hugh was leaning against the stable wall surveying his handiwork. 'You look lovely, Jean,' he told his pony. 'And don't you dare roll when I put you out tonight!'

'Gosh, Hugh, just listen to the rain,' sighed Carol. 'Mrs. Cameron said if it is still raining hard by after supper we can keep the ponies in all night if we want to. Then they won't get wet after all our hard work. So long as we don't mind the mucking out in the morning – and I said we didn't . . .'

'Oh, I don't mind mucking out at all,' agreed Hugh. 'In fact, I rather enjoy it, now I know the right way to go about it.'

The trek was due to start out at ten o'clock next morning. Fortunately, the weather was more promising than it had been the previous afternoon and although it was overcast and dull it was at least dry and the riders set out in high spirits. Mr. Cameron led the trek and his wife brought up the rear, leading Prince, the pack pony.

They wound their way at a fairly leisurely pace through the forest before coming into a cultivated area where there were fields with stock grazing along the banks of the river Druie. Mr. Cameron called a halt and spoke to the party about the need to respect the farmers and crofters over whose land they rode. He told them that it was important always to obtain permission from the owner before riding over his land and that it was essential that all gates were closed after the riders had passed through. No gate must ever be carelessly left open or stock would stray. It was equally important not to ride across the middle of fields where young seeds or crops were sown, or right through the middle of a flock of sheep, some of which might be ewes expecting lambs. In fact, the farmer and his posses- sions must be treated with courtesy and consideration by the rider.

'Now I am going to show you how to open and shut a gate,' said Mr. Cameron. 'It is much easier to do if you know the correct way to go about it. Although we have few gates to open during our rides up here it will be good practice if each member of the party takes his or her turn at opening them.'

Then he took both reins in his right hand and riding his pony alongside the gate reached down and undid the catch with his left hand. This done, Mr. Cameron reined back, drawing the gate open. The pony then stood quite quietly whilst all the trekkers filed through.

'This is where a well-trained pony is most useful,' ex- plained Mr. Cameron. 'So often you see the horse fidget- ing about while its rider is trying to hold the gate open for the rest of the company. We school them to gates when they are quite young.'

One of the trekkers was very busy chatting to the rider immediately behind him and was not paying attention as his pony took him through the gate. They went too close to the gate-post and he got a painful bang on his knee-cap.

When everyone was through Mr. Cameron rode through himself and then brought his pony round again alongside the gate and made him stand quietly while he fastened the catch.

They rode for two hours and then entering a glen they halted for their midday meal and tethered the ponies while they ate. It was cool, which kept away the flies and insects that warm weather bring, but meant that the trekkers soon got cold sitting about in the heather. Very soon they were on their way again, riding in single file along a stony track which wound between magnificent heather-covered hills. The path followed the burn which clattered and babbled over the rocks ceaselessly. In every direction, as far as the eye could see, there was not a sign of human life. The track reached the head of the glen and the trekkers climbed a short, steep, gradient before coming out on a lonely plateau.

It seemed to Carol and Hugh to be the roof of the world. The party paused whilst the ponies rested after their stiff climb and the trekkers gazed about them at the magnificent view. Rolling hills spread out in every direction and far down behind them, the way they had come, they could see the valley that they had just left behind. On a clear day it would have been possible to pick out the Croftmore farm with a pair of powerful binoculars.

Carol slipped off her pony to ease its back for a few moments while she got her wind back. Belle was sweating, despite the chill air on the tops, and her sides heaved as she stood.

'Poor Belle, are you very tired?' Carol slipped her arm affectionately around the pony's neck. Belle snorted in disgust at such a suggestion and tossed her head impatiently to show that she was quite ready to continue when her rider was.

'What a marvellous trek.' Hugh kicked his feet out of the stirrups and leant forward along Jean's neck to rest. 'That was a jolly stiff climb.'

Carol nodded. 'Aren't they wonderfully sure-footed. I thought I was going to slip over Belle's tail once or twice.'

'So did I!' agreed Hugh. 'Thank goodness for the neck-strap and Jean's mane, I hung on to both most of the time.'

It was cold and the party began to descend into the next glen. It was mid-afternoon when Mr. Cameron pointed below to a farm which they could see at the edge of a pine wood in the valley below. This was their destination for the night.

'We shall be there by half past three,' said Hugh.

Mrs. Cameron shook her head. 'It's farther than it looks, Hugh,' she told him. 'Another two miles I should say. Distances can be very deceptive, particularly when viewed from above.'

It rained during the last half hour of the ride and the party were glad to reach the shelter of the farm. The ponies had to be fed and watered and rubbed down before the trekkers were able to enjoy the homely welcome of the Scottish farmstead. It was wonderful after their long day in the saddle to shed damp clothes and enjoy delicious oatcakes and honey and a cup of strong tea, before a cheerful log fire.

The next day they were up and away in good time. Their route was to take them some fifteen miles in the day and a halt for two hours was planned at noon so that the trekkers could visit a Highland Folk Museum. It was a fascinating place and Hugh was particularly interested in the relics it contained. They bought postcards to send home and wrote them sitting in the sun on a bench outside.

'It's dreadful to think that this is my second week already,' sighed Hugh. 'You are lucky to be staying on, Carol. I shall miss you in London – it'll be awful after these two weeks here.'

Carol nodded. 'It doesn't seem fair,' she agreed. 'But still I'm older than you and I have done my share of school. Anyway, perhaps if I'm still here next Easter you could come up then and stay.'

'Gosh, Carol, do you mean to stay as long as that?'

His sister nodded. 'If they'll have me, I'm sure that I shall want to . . .'

'Well, I wouldn't be too sure,' he warned. 'I heard one of the guests saying it's terribly quiet up here in the winter.'

'Not so quiet now that there is ski-ing,' she told him. 'Anyway, I am sure I shall love working with the ponies and I won't mind it being quiet.'

They got up from the bench and went and posted their cards. There was still half an hour to wander about the village before they were due to forgather again where the ponies were tethered. When they did so they found Mr. and Mrs. Cameron studying their maps.

'We are keeping in the valley this afternoon,' said Mrs. Cameron. 'And staying tonight in a guest house in a village similar to this one. We travel along the banks of the river for quite a distance so we may get some trotting and cantering.'

'All up!' commanded Mr. Cameron, folding up his map and packing it away. 'We still have quite a distance to cover.'

He always personally checked each pony's girth before the party moved off. The saddles were not removed unless it was a very hot day, and only the girths were loosened. These had to be drawn up again before the rider mounted. No one was allowed to ride off before the rest of the party was ready. These rules were strictly kept whenever the Camerons took a party out trekking and it was only in this way that their ponies remained obedient and well-behaved.

Bride led by the village mayor

They rode through the village in twos, a pony's length between each couple. Then their route took them through several fields down to the banks of the river. Those who wished to were able to enjoy some trotting and cantering. The cantering was never done all together in a bunch. When the party reached a field which the leaders considered suitable, each rider was allowed off by himself to canter to the far side. Otherwise a stampede would have ensued and nervous riders would have been carried along probably faster than they enjoyed. This is the procedure for faster paces which is followed at many trekking and riding holiday centres.

The afternoon passed very pleasantly, hacking along the banks of the river for several miles until they reached the next village farther down the valley. Here they spent the night at a guest house arriving there early in the evening.

'We had a short day's trekking yesterday,' Mr. Cameron told them as they packed their belongings on their ponies next morning prior to an early start. 'Because we have a long day over the hills ahead of us today. Then tomorrow we shall be back at Croftmore by early afternoon. We have about fourteen miles ahead of us today and it looks as though it's going to be fine.'

A haze hung in the valley, particularly over the river which they had followed the previous day. This was often a sign of a hot day in the Highlands.

'I'm not going to wear my sweater,' said Hugh, rolling it into a bundle and stuffing it into his pack. 'If we are going into the hills and it's really hot, we'll need to strip everything off.'

'But it is still quite cool now,' Carol told him. 'Your macintosh isn't properly rolled. Look, that end is going to be trailing soon and then you won't be popular if we all have to stop and wait while your bundles are packed again.' She looped her pony's rein over her arm and went to help her brother load his pony.

The party left the valley and began to wind its way up into the hills. By ten-thirty the sun was high in a brilliant blue sky and the riders were rolling up their sleeves and enjoying superb views all around them. Here and there white dots could be seen about the heather-covered slopes looking at first like stones, but when they moved Carol could see that they were sheep grazing on free range. How hot they must be in their shaggy coats, she thought. Belle picked her way cleverly up the mountain path, stretching her neck out and using her powerful quarters to climb with her considerable load. The riders had been taught not to interfere with their ponies' mouths when they were climbing. One youth, Peter, who had joined the party at the last moment and who had told the Camerons that he was an experienced trekker, made frequent attempts to catch his pony's head up and even to leave the path and guide the pony through the heather. This was stopped immediately by Mrs. Cameron.

'Keep in your place, Peter!' she commanded. 'Your pony has been taught to follow the others so leave him alone. You can pick your own way through the heather when we get to the top if you want to, but not when we are climbing.'

Peter reluctantly gave up the attempt to branch out on his own. He had been chaffing silently at the slow pace for several days, and Mr. and Mrs. Cameron had been keeping a wary eye on him.

It got very hot. The ponies sweated and the riders fanned themselves with bracken and heather fronds. The party wound slowly through the heather in single file. It was too warm to do more than trek quite slowly.

Suddenly Mr. Cameron reined in his pony and raised his hand. The party halted.

'Deer!' he said and pointed to a slope about a hundred yards from them. At first Carol and Hugh could see nothing. The hillside in front looked empty of everything save heather and occasional rocks and boulders. Mr. Cameron motioned to the party to come up to him quietly.

'Do you see them?' he spoke quietly to his wife. She nodded. She had seen them as soon as her husband had indicated that there were deer ahead. As soon as you knew what to look for they could be quickly picked out by experienced highland dwellers.

On the opposite slope a small burn trickled its way down through the heather. About half-way down Carol could see some small orange-brown shapes. These, so the party was informed, were the deer. As she watched Carol suddenly saw one of the brown shapes move and instantly she could see that it was indeed, a deer. It walked through the heather right to the edge of the burn. As she watched the other shapes began to emerge clearly as deer also and she saw that the hillside was literally covered with them.

Mr. Cameron had dismounted quietly, and slipping his pony's rein over his arm he quickly picked up his telescope and began to watch the deer. Mrs. Cameron, still holding her pack pony Prince, remained in the saddle but scanned the slope through her binoculars.

'They haven't got our wind yet,' she remarked. 'I can only see one small stag, grazing now by the burn. There, he's moved behind that stunted tree.'

'Yes, they're nearly all hinds,' agreed her husband. 'I can see your stag, he is very small, not much more than a knobber. Look, that old hind has her head up and she's watching us . . .'

'Why don't they move away?' hissed Hugh excitedly.

'I thought red deer were so scary and here we are in full view of them and they have not even seen us.'

'They have seen us, at least one or two of the old hinds have,' Mr. Cameron told him. 'They are the keepers of the herds, not the stags. There are always one or two hinds who are on the alert and don't miss much. But you see they haven't got our wind yet. If we had come up the other side of the slope they would have scented us before we saw them and they would have moved off immediately. Here, Hugh, jump off Jean and take a look at them through the telescope.'

Mrs. Cameron had been watching the hillside through her binoculars. 'There is a big stag,' she said slowly. 'He is lying down some distance away from the rest of the herd, look, in the heather well to the left near that big old hind who is watching us. Hullo, here come some more, they're on the alert, coming up the slope.'

'Yes, I see them,' replied Mr. Cameron, and they could be plainly seen with the naked eye coming up from below the main herd. 'They must have been below us and we never saw them. I expect they got our wind or heard us talking. Look, they will take the other deer with them now.'

All the deer had stopped feeding and stood with heads high watching the trekkers. As the new parcel of deer joined them and proceeded up the slope and on to skyline they all began to move slowly away too, heads held unnaturally high and white tails plainly to be seen as they walked with a strange, stilted, gait up the hill. Several deer emerged suddenly out of the heather where the trekkers had not seen them until they moved.

Last to leave was the big stag. When he stood up the trekkers could all see him plainly, his huge antlered head turned to watch them scornfully. As his harem departed one by one up the hillside and over the skyline he suddenly decided that it was time for him to leave too. With head held high he walked quickly away and moved up on to the skyline. There he paused and his head looked magnificent as he stared across the valley at the intruders to his kingdom. Then he turned and strode away after his hinds.

'Oh dear, they've gone!' sighed Hugh. 'Didn't he look marvellous.'

'Don't worry, we'll probably see more before the day is over,' promised Mr. Cameron. 'These hills are full of them.' He slipped his telescope back into its leather case and pulled his pony's head up from where it was trying to graze. 'Another mile or two and then we shall stop for lunch.'

Lunch was glorious, eaten on top of the world. Or so it seemed to Carol and Hugh. It was blazing hot without a breath of wind. They drank mugfuls of clear burn water.

Peter had brought his own map and was anxious to leave the main party and find his own way to the rendezvous for the night. It was a beautiful clear day and he pointed out that he couldn't possibly lose his way. He wanted a closer look at some deer and they couldn't get close with so many of them.

Mr. and Mrs. Cameron were adamant in refusing his request. He must keep with the rest of the party. He was their responsibility and the pony was a valuable trekker. They didn't want it lamed or Peter lost. Peter persisted that he knew this range of hills and that he was seventeen and quite old enough to look after himself.

It was unpleasant and Peter looked very disgruntled when the leaders still refused to let him go. Carol thought how silly and unkind it was of him to spoil such a marvellous ride by being dissatisfied. It had been made quite clear at the beginning of the trek, she knew, that riders were to keep together and not go off on their own.

. . . Wanted to leave the party

During the afternoon it seemed to get hotter and hotter.
The party proceeded over the hills at a leisurely pace. Far
away a faint rumbling was suddenly heard and along the
skyline a dark bank of cloud was seen to be building
up.

'Thunder!' called out Mr. Cameron. 'I thought we were
in for a storm. Hope it doesn't break before we get down.'

'It's a long way away yet,' called out Mrs. Cameron.
'And we have only another three miles or so, we should
easily get to our farm. Peter, come back on to the track!'
she spoke sharply to the lad. They were just beginning to
descend a steep slope and he had pulled his pony away
from the others and was pushing it downwards through
the heather.

'I will in a minute,' he retorted rudely. 'I just want to
go over to that rock for a look at that hill for deer.' He

kicked his pony hard and it shuffled along so that he was quickly out of earshot.

Mr. and Mrs. Cameron exchanged glances. Carol could see that they were both furious. Mrs. Cameron was prevented from following him by her pack pony as Peter very well knew. She couldn't trot over treacherous rock-strewn ground with a pack pony in tow. Neither did Mr. Cameron wish to leave his position in the lead when they were half-way down a slope. This would endanger the rest of the party straggling down behind him, each pony dutifully following the one in front of it.

They continued down the slope, watching Peter as they went. He had reached his rock, and jumping defiantly off his pony he climbed on to the boulder and surveyed the scene around him. The pony stood with dilated nostrils blowing hard, his sides heaving after trotting over the rough ground in the heat. Suddenly it lifted its head and looked back at the rest of the party some forty yards away.

Peter suddenly realized he had not kept hold of his reins and that his pony might decide to join the party again, leaving him stranded and very undignified. He slid immediately off the boulder and grabbed the pony's rein. It snorted and tossed its head in astonishment. Peter vaulted into the saddle again. He waved to the party and shouted across to them that he was going to make for another spot farther down the hill.

He set off downhill at a walk, the pony stretched its neck out to balance itself and the boy pulled its head up immediately and kicked it hard. Before him, he could see what looked like a clear stretch of heather and he began to push the pony forward at a trot. They shambled awkwardly off down the hill.

The Camerons halted their party and stood staring in horror after him. They could see their precious pony being made to trot down what was very likely rockstrewn or boggy ground.

'Damn the boy . . .' muttered Mr. Cameron. 'He'll lame that pony at the rate he's going.'

Just as he spoke the pony suddenly tripped over a hidden rock and in a minute was down on its knees. Peter,

. . . Was down on its knees

who had been rolling insecurely in the saddle, shot forward up the pony's neck and did a complete somersault straight over its head.

Hugh, sitting frozen with horror on Jean's back, longed to shout 'Hooray!' but one glance at Mr. Cameron's tight-lipped, angry, face silenced him. The pony scrambled immediately to its feet and finding its rider gone and the reins pulled over its head, it set off at a mad gallop down the hill, the saddle packs bumping up and down ridiculously as it went and the reins swinging dangerously around its legs. Then, it must have trodden on a rein because it slipped suddenly and slithered sideways on to its haunches. With a quick twist it righted itself and proceeded on more slowly, but everyone could see that it was limping badly.

'Oh, you wretched boy . . .' Carol heard Mrs. Cameron mutter as she watched her pony stumbling painfully on.

Peter had got slowly to his feet. He rubbed his head and watched his mount ruefully. Reaching the valley below them the pony paused. Its sides heaved up and down and it looked around. The trekkers could plainly see that its rein was now snapped. Mr. Cameron slipped quickly off his pony. He handed his rein to Carol.

'Come on down very slowly,' he told her. 'I'm going to catch that pony before it damages itself any more.' He set off quickly down the hill through the heather, passing Peter without a word as the boy stood sheepishly by the rock.

The pony in the valley below had begun to walk slowly on, dragging a hind leg and trailing its broken rein, dropping its head now and again to blow at a patch of ground and shaking its thick tousled mane.

CHAPTER SEVEN

CAROL STARTS TO WORK

By the time the runaway pony had been caught and the party gathered in the valley below, nearly an hour had passed. The day had ended in tragedy and nobody dared speak to Mr. and Mrs. Cameron who were furious with Peter.

Carol saw Mrs. Cameron glance anxiously at the dark banks of cloud which had been gathering ominously during the last half-hour. Mr. Cameron changed places with his wife and she led the trek with Prince, the pack pony in tow, and Mr. Cameron followed very slowly, getting farther and farther behind the main party, leading the limping pony with Peter bringing up the rear on foot.

'I bet he's feeling awful,' Hugh whispered to his sister.

Carol nodded. 'Silly ass!' she hissed back. 'He ought to have known better. He deserves all he gets.'

Hugh shivered suddenly. 'Gosh, it's getting quite cold. Look at those clouds, Carol, I think we're going to get caught out in it.'

'So do I.'

They hurried on as fast as it was possible along the stony track. Now and again the rumbling of thunder came to them, louder and more threatening than before. At last their way took them off the hill down into the tree line, and as they left the open moors a sudden bright flash lit up the pine trees and the forest with startling clearness.

'Lightning!' exclaimed Hugh.

'Of course it is, silly!' groaned Carol. She hated thunder and lightning and it was frightening to be caught amongst these ghostly pines. A loud clap of thunder cracked overhead and the ponies bunched up together, twitching their ears and tucking in their tails. The riders had put on their macintoshes half an hour earlier and they shivered and turned up their coat collars.

'Keep together!' called out Mrs. Cameron. 'We're nearly down now. Only another mile till we reach the farm. Don't anyone get separated from the others.' They proceeded down through the forest. It grew darker and darker and then again a vivid flash lit their way for an instant. Carol tightened her hold on Belle's reins as she waited for the crash of thunder which would inevitably follow the flash. When it came, it sounded right overhead and the ponies trembled with fear.

They straggled on down through the trees. 'How much farther?' someone shouted out plaintively to the leader.

'Nearly there!' she yelled back.

'Here comes the rain!' cried Hugh, and as they left the forest and came out on to open moorland again, the first big drops of rain began to fall.

'There's the farm!' Mrs. Cameron was pointing ahead to where they could just see a welcoming cluster of buildings in the semi-darkness.

'Let's hurry,' someone shouted. 'We're going to get soaked!'

But Mrs. Cameron would not allow the trekkers to stampede over the heather for the shelter of the farm. It was just as well that she didn't, for whilst they crossed the stretch of open ground, another thunder-clap broke overhead and the ponies might easily have bolted. The riders bunched in behind the leader and the heavy drops began to come faster. Soon it seemed as though the heavens had opened. The rain poured down in a steady drenching sheet and within a few minutes ponies and riders were soaked.

At last they turned in to the sanctuary of their night's lodging. The farmer and his wife were waiting in the big warm friendly barn to welcome them. The riders crowded into it and sighed with relief.

'I've never been so glad to come to the end of a ride,' said Carol as she climbed shakily out of the saddle and shook herself like a dog. She had also never in her life, coming from a town as they did, experienced such drenching rain.

The farmer was fussing around them. He had been very worried when the storm broke and the trekkers did not arrive. Everyone felt very concerned about Mr. Cameron and Peter and the lame pony.

'Angus will be all right,' Mrs. Cameron promised them. 'He wouldn't want anyone to turn out in this rain and there's nothing we could do for them anyway. They won't be long I'm sure. What we've got to do now is to get these ponies stabled and fed and ourselves into dry clothes.'

There was much to be done. Each pony was tied in a stall in the cow byre and the saddles removed. Their backs steamed and their tails and manes hung limp and drenched. When their bridles were slipped off they shook their heads and a shower of drops fell from their ears and forelocks. The storm raged on outside, with now and again a vivid flash lighting the interior of the barn and then a resounding crash broke over the farm. But now, in the warmth and safety of the improvised stables the riders called out and chaffed one another and rubbed their ponies over with wisps made of hay and straw.

Carol had fed Belle, who was nuzzling eagerly into her manger and making little contented nickers of delight, and was ready to cross the yard to the farm with her bundle of belongings when there was the sound of hooves on the cobbles outside. There, at last, was Mr. Cameron and Peter and the lame pony, all looking like drowned rats. It was a relief to see them safe and no time was lost in making the unfortunate frightened pony warm and comfortable. The claps of thunder were beginning to come less frequently and sounded farther away but the rain continued to pour down.

The trekkers put their heads down and bolted across the open yard for the house. It was glorious to relax in a hot bath and to chat about the day's adventures before a roaring fire.

'I wonder what they will do to Peter,' said Hugh with relish. 'Gosh, I wouldn't like to be in his shoes tonight!'

'Oh nothing, he's learnt his lesson,' replied Carol. 'I expect they'll send him home tomorrow. The damage is done now and he will know better next time – if there is a next time.'

Peter left the next day but the transport of the lame pony was not so easy. It was quite incapable of walking the last fourteen miles home and so a wagon had to be hired to convey the casualty.

After the night of rain a watery sun had appeared and the trekkers turned out to enjoy their last day of the tour. The distance home was not a long one and it was planned that the party should reach Croftmore by mid-afternoon at the latest. The farm lane and the gateways were soon churned into mud after the night's heavy rain and the bracken and trees and heather were soaked and glistening with the wet. They did not need to go up to the hills that day for their way took them along the valley towards home.

Hugh had only two days of his holiday at Croftmore left. He hoped that he would be able to spend them trekking in the Cairngorm mountains.

'I hope they won't think the ponies are too tired,' he said to Carol as they jogged along the banks of the river.

'Oh, no, they're fit after all this work,' replied Carol. 'Mrs. Cameron told me that treks would be going out as usual for the last two days of this week. These ponies are so well fed that they thrive on hard work. After you've gone I won't get so much riding. Apparently, they are fully booked for the next six weeks.'

'Someone else will have Belle to look after,' Hugh reminded his sister.

'Oh, yes, I know,' she replied. 'But still I shall probably be able to ride her a bit during the winter. Anyway, it will be quite fun to ride some of the other ponies as well.' She patted the pony affectionately. 'I think she knows we are nearly home, she seems full of beans this morning.'

Mrs. Cameron indicated that those who wished might have a short canter. Hugh climbed clumsily up his reins and crouched over Jean's neck and dug his heels into her sides. The pony bounded forward and set off at a fair pace.

'Sit up, Hugh!' shouted Mrs. Cameron. 'You aren't a jockey . . .' She rode alongside him. 'Keep your hands down and try and grip the saddle with your knees and don't let her gallop, this isn't a race.'

They proceeded at a hard canter and arrived breathless and rather disorganized at the clump of trees where they had been told to halt. Hugh had lost his stirrups and various members of the party were looking dishevelled. Head scarves had gone awry and reins were flapping. The ponies must have sensed that they were nearing their home ground because they needed no urging. There was a pause whilst the leaders of the trek busied themselves getting the party back into shape. Feet were slipped back into stirrup irons, headgear was straightened and the riders settled themselves into their saddles again.

'Another half-hour riding and then we shall stop for

lunch,' said Mr. Cameron. 'Oh, look, there are some Highland cattle down by the river . . .'

Three shaggy beasts were down at the water's edge. Their thick long chestnut hair hung down, nearly touching the ground, and their noble heads were surmounted by immense horns. They gazed unmoved at the trekkers, some of whom were eager to photograph them.

'Don't they look dramatic,' said Carol. 'But I don't think I should like to go too close. Are they as fierce as they look?'

'Some of them can be unfriendly,' replied Mr. Cameron. 'Especially when they have young calves. But these three don't seem very disturbed, you'll be all right if you don't get too close.'

'Don't worry, I shan't do that,' promised Carol, looking at the wicked points of the sweeping horns which adorned the cows' heads.

'There are more of these cattle in the highlands now than there were fifty years ago,' Mr. Cameron told them. 'Several Scottish lairds have got herds roaming on their estates and they are quite a familiar sight in some districts.'

The sun continued to shine fitfully and the trekkers enjoyed a pleasant hack home through the beautiful pine forest of Rothiemurcus. They reached Croftmore about three o'clock in the afternoon. The ponies grazing in the fields around the farm looked up when the party approached. Some of the youngsters cantered across to greet them with whinnies of pleasure. Their manes and tails flowed out gracefully in the breeze and they tossed their pretty highland heads. There were two brood mares with diminutive foals at foot. They raised their heads to watch the party whilst their youngsters high-stepped excitedly about their mothers, their dun-coloured coats and woolly tails making a delightful picture. The foals would have liked to urge their mothers to join the

They raised their heads

reception party at the paddock railings. They cantered a short distance with their small heads held high and tiny ears pricked, and then wheeled about and retreated again to pause in the security of their mothers' ample flanks.

'Those two little fellows have got to be halter-broken this coming winter,' Mr. Cameron told Carol. 'That will be a job that you can help us with. We have a full programme of schooling ahead for the next six months so you're going to be kept busy.'

'That will be splendid,' replied Carol. 'But I'm afraid I've never worked with young ponies before so I hope I shall be of help to you.'

'Oh, you will soon learn,' he told her. 'It will be grand for my wife to have an assistant. Once our visitors have departed I shall have to get down to a bit of farming again.'

When the ponies had been fed and turned out on their home pastures to graze, the trekking party spent the hour after tea cleaning tack. Girths and stirrup leathers had got very muddy after the storm. It was satisfying to see each saddle and bridle washed and dried and well soaped, hanging on its respective peg.

'We've certainly seen a bit of Scotland during this last three days,' said Hugh, tidying Jean's stall and stowing the grooming kit away in the box under the manger. 'I'm going to mark our route on the map Daddy gave me. We must have covered nearly fifty miles or more.'

'Easily fifty miles, I should say,' replied his sister. 'But come on now, Hughie, it's after six o'clock and I want to change. There's a party going in to the cinema at Grantown in the Land-Rover tonight and I'd rather like to go.'

Two days later Carol went to the station to say goodbye to her brother. It was sad to see Hugh leave but she knew he would report favourably to her parents about the success of their venture. After he had left, her day's work followed a general routine and for at least a week she did not go out riding at all. She tried to work hard to learn about an operator's work in a busy trekking centre. The house was full of visitors because it was still a peak holiday period and daily guests visited the centre for rides as well. Sometimes these casual riders did not wish to do any stable work at all and preferred to arrive in the stable-yard and find their pony clean and ready for them to mount. These ponies were Carol's responsibility and she had to work fast to get several animals fed and groomed and saddled by ten o'clock in the morning.

After the day's trek had departed she would go down to the field where the young stock and the mares were turned out. Each day it was necessary for someone to check over these animals to be sure that none was lame from having picked up a stone or from a playful kick from one of its fellows. Water had to be checked and where it was supplied in troughs these had to be cleaned of leaves and sticks. Any litter which had been thrown into the fields by careless hikers in the form of old tins or cartons had to be picked up. Carol enjoyed these daily visits to the ponies and when they would let her she handled each pony, particularly the two foals. Mrs. Cameron had asked her to do this but she was strictly forbidden to give them titbits. Young foals, especially colts, would pick up bad habits if they were used to being fed by visitors. The eager nuzzling of the tiny velvet muzzles could quickly become an unpleasant nuisance when they began to nip and even to bite the well-meaning donor if the food was not forthcoming quickly.

Soon the two foals ceased to tremble and start when she rubbed their little woolly necks and fondled their ears and wispy manes. This she had been told to do as a preliminary to slipping on the halters. Ideally, a foal that is to be broken for trekking purposes should be handled from birth, but in many trekking centres this is not possible because the operators are too busy during the youngsters' earliest months, which naturally fall during the summer.

Both foals were bred from pure Highland stock and had the characteristic dun coat and black points of the breed. One of the yearlings was going to be grey but at the moment her coat was still nearly black. This in time would grow lighter and she could easily be nearly white by the time she was three years old. Mares in foal received additional feeding if the grass was not rich, but the two present matrons looked fat and prosperous and their children were fast becoming weaned.

After Carol had spent about half an hour visiting the

ponies and checking that all was well she returned to the yard and tidied the stalls. Sweeping up was a heavy job and one that she found very tiring at first but after a while she learnt how to do it without exhausting herself too much. Mangers had to be cleaned, water buckets filled and the tack-room tidied. Sometimes the riders returned at lunch-time, especially if the weather was bad or if they were visitors from a near-by hotel, and then Carol was busy unsaddling the ponies and helping those who needed assistance.

After lunch, unless there was another ride going out, she was free for an hour or two. She seldom spent the time indoors but sometimes cycled to Aviemore to do some shopping or took Mrs. Cameron's two terriers for a walk.

Then the day trek would return and the yard became a buzz of activity again. Carol only had time for a hurried cup of tea before starting on the tack cleaning. She soon learnt to do this more quickly than she had at first. She got to know where each strap and buckle fitted and which way to put the stirrup irons on and how to fold the girths. Once a week she had to wash and saddle soap all the head collars and scrub the water buckets. The Croftmore premises were not grand but they were kept scrupulously clean and tidy.

The lame pony was being kept in a loose box. He was a grey native pony and he was to be kept indoors for several weeks. Carol mucked out his box and daily massaged his hock. She took great pains to try and keep him clean but his coat got very stained because he lay down a lot to rest his aching leg. When he began to mend he was to be turned out to rest for six months. Peter's escapade had proved an expensive one for the Camerons.

On Sundays all the ponies were rested, and although Carol had the lame pony to look after and some of the others to feed, she was free for most of the day. Sometimes one of the guests invited her to join them for an outing by car or for a walk to Glenmore. A ski-lift had been erected on Cairngorm and this operated all summer for the benefit of visitors who wished to be carried up the mountain to enjoy the superb views. Carol found this a stimulating experience although a very cold one, as she sat in the little chair and swung up the side of the hill.

After learning the daily routine work she was sometimes able to join a trek if all the ponies were not booked. Belle was very popular and it was some weeks before she got the chance to ride her again but she enjoyed trying the different ponies. Whether she joined Mr. Cameron's advanced or Mrs. Cameron's beginners' ride, it was her job to bring up the rear and to give help where it was needed.

In September two children arrived to spend a fortnight by themselves at Croftmore. Sisters of ten and twelve, they had done only a little riding before. Several good trekking centres advertise that they welcome children by themselves and there is no doubt that for a keen young rider it can be a grand holiday. But, of course, it is very important that they should be sent only to a recognized and approved establishment where the proprietors are experienced with children and are prepared to take the responsibility of them.

Carol found the company of the two girls very pleasant. Mrs. Cameron had put her nominally in charge of them and she felt responsible for seeing that they changed out of wet clothes and went to bed at the right time and did not get over-tired with too much riding. They were mad about the ponies and would have ridden all day if they had been allowed to. They quickly learnt how to groom their ponies and how to clean their tack. They put some of the older riders to shame by their zeal. During spare hours they followed Carol about, helping her with her tasks and plying her with questions. She missed them very much when they left and there was no doubt that they had had the best holiday of their young lives.

One Sunday morning in late September, whilst Carol was enjoying a leisurely breakfast with the few guests who were staying, Mrs. Cameron came into the dining-room with a catalogue in her hand.

'Carol, this is the catalogue for the Kelso Horse Sales which are held in the border country twice a year.' She pulled out a chair and settled herself beside her assistant. 'There are several highland ponies I am interested in. How about coming down with me to the Sales at the end of this month!'

'Gosh, how simply marvellous!' Carol was thrilled at the news. 'But can we leave here?'

'Yes, I think so,' she replied. 'It is the end of the season and I think I only have two bookings. Angus will look after them for us. We cannot both leave the farm at the moment but you and I could and it would teach you a great deal.'

'I'd simply love to come,' said Carol. 'I can't think of anything I should enjoy more. Will we go by train or drive and shall we have to stay overnight?'

Mrs. Cameron laughed. 'Well, I'm glad you are so enthusiastic. Yes, we shall have to stay at least one night and we shall drive. In the Land-Rover if you can bear the draught and the bumps. I need more saddlery and they sell some good stuff at Kelso and the Land-Rover would be convenient to bring it back in.'

'Oh, I shall look forward to coming so much,' said Carol. 'And I suppose we might even buy a pony?'

'Yes, we might easily!' agreed Mrs. Cameron. 'But don't let the news spoil your breakfast. Have some more coffee and read this while you do so, it tells you all about the different horses and ponies which will be offered for sale.' She handed Carol the Sale catalogue. It was a fat publication which listed some eighty animals. Carol thumbed through it with keen interest.

'My goodness,' she said. 'We should be able to find a new trekking pony out of all this lot.'

CHAPTER EIGHT

AT THE HORSE SALES

CAROL and Mrs. Cameron left Aviemore in the Land-Rover to drive south to Kelso, the day before the Sales were to be held. It was pleasant to drive through the same places that she had seen on her journey north in the train nearly two months earlier. Kingussie, Newtonmore, Dalwhinnie, Blair Atholl, these names would mean much more now that she had driven through the villages instead of just viewing them from the train.

At Blair Atholl they stopped and spent an hour at Blair Castle, the seat of the Duke of Atholl. They toured the apartments with a guide and Carol enjoyed seeing one of the greatest Scottish castles which was steeped in legend and history. When they drove away along the tree-lined drive to the gates of the castle Mrs. Cameron told Carol about the Duke's ponies.

'This is one of the best pony-trekking centres in Scotland now,' she said. 'The Duke of Atholl has some very fine Highland ponies and these he kindly loans for trekking.'

As she spoke they saw a party of riders approaching them. They were mounted on large dun-coloured ponies and were returning from a morning ride in the grounds of the castle. They got out of the Land-Rover and watched them pass with keen interest. It was the end of the summer season but the ponies looked fit and well.

Continuing the drive south they ate their picnic lunch

at the Pass of Killiecrankie, a famous beauty-spot and the scene of an ancient battle. They did not stop in Perth but continued to the Queensferry, a few miles north of Edinburgh, which they reached by four o'clock. It was pleasant to get out and stretch their legs whilst they were on the ferry and to admire the immense structure of the new road bridge which was nearly completed. There were several miles of approach roads being constructed too and this tremendous undertaking had taken some years to carry out.

'We shall miss the ferries when the new bridge is ready,' said Mrs. Cameron as they stood on the top deck of the car ferry and watched the wash foaming out behind them. 'But there is no doubt that it will shorten our journey south. Sometimes during peak holiday periods the ferries are very busy and there are long queues by the time we can get down here.'

'How much farther is it to Kelso?' asked Carol, pulling up her coat collar against the wind which was whipping across the ferry.

'About an hour and a half, I think,' replied Mrs. Cameron. 'We should be there by six o'clock. I want to have an early night because we've got a very heavy day ahead of us tomorrow.'

'When do you plan to leave for home?'

'Not later than four o'clock and earlier if possible,' she replied. 'I have studied the catalogue and the "lots" that we are interested in come on during the morning.'

'We shall have to get on to the ground early tomorrow,' said Carol.

'Certainly we will,' agreed Mrs. Cameron. 'But that will not be a hardship, our hotel is very close to the sale ground. I hope you won't get too tired with such a long journey home, but I don't want to be away from the farm too long at the moment.'

'I don't mind at all,' replied Carol. 'You are the one who is driving, so it's much more tiring for you. I have very much enjoyed today.'

Next morning they were up early and on the sale ground by eight-thirty. Mrs. Cameron made her way at once to the saddlery enclosure where saddles, bridles, rugs, leathers, girths and various other items were laid out for inspection by would-be purchasers. She went over various items very carefully, checking them for signs of wear and lifting the saddles for weight. There was some good-quality equipment and she was able to obtain two saddles and three bridles which were in good condition and perfectly suitable for pony-trekking purposes.

Carol meanwhile had been strolling up and down the pony lines studying particularly the animals which were marked in the catalogue. There were many half-bred ponies of no particular breed but a feature of the sale were the pure-bred representatives of several native breeds.

She was delighted to see some Fell ponies and remembered with pleasure the holiday they had spent the previous summer trekking in Northumberland. She wondered whether she could persuade Mrs. Cameron to buy a Fell pony for her stable. She was sure it would be perfectly suitable for the country around Croftmore. There were several Shetland ponies and some Welsh Mountain ponies and a strong turn-out of Highlanders. Mrs. Cameron had marked two nice-looking young grey ponies and Carol was inspecting them with what she hoped was an intelligent look.

Mrs. Cameron soon joined her. She asked for the ponies to be brought out for examination and she went over each of them thoroughly, looking in their mouths, feeling their legs and inspecting them with an expert eye. She liked them both.

Fell ponies at Kelso

'Hop up and try this one, Carol,' she said. 'He is a splendid-looking pony and has a good reputation. I'm afraid he may fetch too much for my pocket, though.'

Carol mounted the pony and rode it carefully about in a figure of eight. It was very obedient to the aids and surprisingly light to respond despite its characteristic heavy build. She could feel it snatch playfully at the bit as she turned it to canter back to the pony lines and wondered whether it would be quite suitable for beginners.

'The pony is very fit,' remarked Mrs. Cameron to the owner. She had noticed the pony's high spirits.

'My daughter has used the pony all this summer holidays,' he replied. 'He is a grand jumper, as nimble as a cat. Some people won't believe it of a Highland pony until they see him with their own eyes.'

Mrs. Cameron nodded. 'I can well believe it,' she said. 'I have nearly thirty Highlanders so I know their capabilities . . .'

The owner looked pleased and called out to Carol to put the pony over a practice fence which had been erected on the ground. Carol, of course, had never jumped more than a ditch in her life before and she hesitated because she did not want to give a display of ignorance or to take a toss.

Mrs. Cameron shook her head. 'No, Carol!' she called out. 'This is not the time or place to learn to jump. Bring the pony over here and get up on the other one.'

Carol, very relieved, rode over and jumped off the pony.

'He is a lovely animal,' said Mrs. Cameron, patting the pony's strong neck. 'But, I think, apart from the price, he might not be quite suitable for my establishment.'

The owner looked disappointed. 'He would carry up to twelve stones and very clever in rough country,' he told her. 'I've put a reserve price of one hundred guineas on him.'

'He's worth that,' replied Mrs. Cameron, 'and I shan't be surprised if you get more. Now, Carol, let's see what you make of this one.'

The second pony was not so good-looking as the first one. He was older and nearly white in colour but he was a pleasant ride and Carol liked his steady pace and felt that he was sensible and more suited to a trekking centre. Mrs. Cameron liked him too. She rode him herself and found that, so far as she could tell, his only fault was rather a hard mouth.

'I don't think I could do very much to correct that at his age,' she remarked to Carol when she had dismounted. 'But he responds adequately and looks as though he would be ideal for trekking. He is a bit older than I would like but he shouldn't fetch more than sixty or seventy guineas.'

They noted the times that these two ponies were scheduled to enter the auction ring and then continued up the pony lines.

'There is so much to see and so little time,' said Carol as Mrs. Cameron hurried her past a tiny coal-black Shetland stallion which had caught her eye. 'I would love to have a look at the hunters but I must not miss a moment at the ringside.'

'We shall have to go to the pony ring soon,' agreed Mrs. Cameron. 'I can see a crowd gathering now so it must be nearly eleven o'clock. I should have enjoyed the horses too but today, alas, there is no time to concentrate on anything but ponies.'

'Never mind!' laughed Carol. 'It's heaven to be spending the day doing that. By the way, I do want you to see the Fell ponies. Look, they are just here . . .'

There were several fine representatives of the Fell pony studs in Northumberland. Mrs. Cameron was immediately interested.

'What grand-looking ponies they are,' she agreed. 'Not at all unlike our Highlanders. I wonder what Angus would say if I brought him one of these back. We could certainly do with another weight-carrier in the stable.'

They admired the Fell ponies and then Mrs. Cameron said that they must find two more ponies that she had marked in her catalogue. After a search they located them, being tried by several prospective buyers. They examined the ponies and both rode one of them but neither was suitable for trekking.

'I don't like the look of that pony's pastern,' said Mrs. Cameron. 'And she's not got a true native head. She's making a noise too . . .'

'What?'

'Bad wind, at least it sounded fishy to me and she hasn't a vet's certificate. I don't want to pay a big price for a pony with poor wind.'

'What about the other pony, the chestnut?' asked Carol.

'Well, I know we didn't ride her,' explained Mrs. Cameron. 'But I could see she was going to get plenty of bids, there was quite a queue waiting to try her. I liked her and she might have been useful for the children who come to Croftmore. But she'll fetch a big price. I hear she has a good reputation. She is on the light side and not up to very much weight so I think Angus would have felt she was too much of an extravagance for our establishment.' They began to walk over to the pony ring where selling was already in progress. 'Never mind, Carol, I think we may get that light grey gelding at a price I can manage – the second one you tried.'

Carol nodded agreement. 'I certainly think he was the most suitable for us. After all, a nice sensible Highland pony is what you need and that's what he seemed to be.'

They joined the throng around the ring. A pony was being paraded round the enclosure and the auctioneer was keeping the bidding brisk. The owner of the pony stood self-consciously just behind the auctioneer. Carol wondered how he must feel, watching his pony parading round and wondering how it was going to end, all within the space of a few minutes. Would the pony get a good home and how many pounds was it going to fetch? It seemed such a gamble.

They consulted their catalogues and managed to find a space for themselves on the rails. Carol was amazed at how quick the auctioneer was. She wondered how he could tell when anyone was making a bid.

'I daren't move in case he thinks I'm bidding,' she whispered. 'No one seems to be shouting out when they want to attract his attention.'

'There isn't any need to do that,' answered Mrs. Cameron. 'Watch me when I bid for that pony we want, it comes in quite soon. Oh, look, Carol, here is that lovely grey you tried. She is a beauty, quite one of the best Highland types.'

'She's lovely,' agreed Carol. 'Look, there is her owner climbing up behind the auctioneer. I wonder what price she will fetch . . .'

They watched the bidding grow higher and higher. When it passed 100 guineas Carol was sure she could see a flicker of relief pass over the owner's inscrutable features. The pony was knocked down at 120 guineas. The owner then looked unmistakably pleased and slipped away to meet the new buyer. Carol hoped that he, or she, was nice.

When the pony came in that they were hoping to buy, Carol's heart began to beat fast with excitement. Mrs. Cameron seemed, outwardly, quite calm and she watched her raise her catalogue when the bidding started at 20 guineas. Rather slowly it climbed higher until at 50 guineas there was a pause and Carol, gripping the rails with excitement, was sure that the pony was theirs already. But suddenly a fresh bid was made and the price rose steeply to 75 guineas within a matter of minutes. Then a few seconds later the hammer was down and the pony sold. Carol's heart dropped to her boots.

'Oh dear, we've lost him,' she whispered sadly.

Mrs. Cameron raised her eyebrows. 'I don't think so,'

she remarked calmly, and nodded across to the auctioneer. 'Come on, Carol, that pony is ours now.'

It was amazing that she had made the final bid and Carol had not even realized it. They elbowed their way through the spectators packed round the ringside and hurried off to see their new pony. He was quietly cropping the grass whilst his owner stood talking to friends and looking pleased with the prices his ponies had fetched.

'Delighted you got him, ma'am,' he said as they came up. 'He'll be a splendid pony for your purpose, I'm sure.'

'I hope so,' agreed Mrs. Cameron. 'I'm very pleased we got him, anyway.' The pony lifted his head and blew gently through his nostrils at them and swished his tail across his hocks.

Carol hugged him delightedly. 'He's perfect!' she exclaimed. The pony pushed against her expectantly. 'What is his name?'

'Swallow.'

'Oh, what a nice name,' said Mrs. Cameron. 'Now I must arrange about sending him north.'

A group of Fell ponies were being brought across to the sale ring. Several more that they had not seen earlier in the day in the lines had appeared. Carol was watching them as she held the grey pony. Mrs. Cameron, who had finished arrangements with the pony's previous owner, suddenly nudged Carol.

'Look at that big pony, Carol, he looks a grand cob.'

A large black Fell pony with a luxuriously thick mane and tail was stepping proudly in the rear of the group.

'He is rather handsome,' agreed Carol.

'I wonder if he is pure-bred Fell,' said Mrs. Cameron. 'Let's go and find out, shall we?'

They walked over and admired the pony. He came from the Linnel stud in Northumberland. He was a seven-year-old black gelding and up to a lot of weight.

'I must sell him because I am overstocked,' explained the lady who was leading him. 'He is a big pony for my purpose, he would carry a man all day.'

'Yes, he looks as though he would,' agreed Mrs. Cameron, inspecting the pony with a critical eye. 'I wonder what my husband would say if I brought him back a Fell pony. We come from the highlands,' she explained, 'and have always been very faithful to our own breed.'

'Oh, I love a Highland pony too,' the lady agreed. 'But, of course, I've always owned my own native breed. I have put a reserve on this pony, Jet, but I hope he will reach eighty guineas.'

Reluctantly they left the sale ring, and leading their new pony they crossed the field to where a refreshment tent had been erected, taking Swallow with them.

'I should have been too tempted to buy that pony if we had gone back to the ringside,' explained Mrs. Cameron ruefully.

Half an hour later they began to walk back to the pony lines.

'I have arranged that Swallow shall travel north tonight so we must find the wagon he will travel in,' said Mrs. Cameron. 'Then, Carol, I think we must be heading north ourselves soon. It's two o'clock already.'

'Look, there's that pony Jet again,' cried Carol. 'Coming away from the sale ring. I wonder who has bought him.'

'So do I,' said Mrs. Cameron. 'He is still with his previous owner.'

'Perhaps he didn't reach the reserve price . . .'

'That's what I am wondering,' agreed Mrs. Cameron. 'Come on, Carol, let's go over and find out. I like that pony and Angus really could do with a weight carrier.'

The pony had been withdrawn at seventy guineas.

Mrs. Cameron asked whether she might ride him. This was readily agreed upon. Animals which didn't reach the reserve price which their owners had put on them were often sold privately afterwards outside the ring.

Mrs. Cameron mounted the pony. Carol could hardly contain her excitement. She knew how keen she must be about the pony if she was actually trying it. Mrs. Cameron rode him hard for ten minutes. She put him through every pace and ended up by popping him over a small jump. Then she rode back to where Carol and Swallow and Jet's owner were waiting.

She jumped off and patted the pony's damp neck. She felt his legs and looked at his teeth. Then she straightened up and smiled.

'I like him a lot,' she said. 'I'll give you eighty guineas and promise him a really good home.'

'I like him very much.'

The deal was quickly done. Jet, the Fell pony from Northumberland was going to make his new home in the highlands of Scotland. Carol was thrilled. He was a handsome black and would look very fine amongst all the duns and greys and chestnuts of the Croftmore establishment.

'Isn't that wonderful!'

'Simply splendid,' agreed Mrs. Cameron. 'I liked the pony as soon as I saw him.'

'Won't Mr. Cameron get a surprise . . .'

'My goodness, won't he!' agreed Mrs. Cameron. 'He'll be sure to come with me next time to keep an eye on me. But I do think he seems just the animal for Angus and not expensive. I think he will be strong when he is fit and in full work, but, of course, that won't worry Angus at all. He likes a pony which keeps up to the bit, he never could be bothered with the lazy ones.'

'We had better arrange that he travels north with Swallow,' suggested Carol.

'Yes, indeed we must,' she agreed. 'Come along, we will see to it at once. If we are going home tonight we mustn't be too long ourselves.'

They walked away across the field to the transport park, leading the two ponies and feeling very excited and satisfied with the way the day had turned out.

An hour later they climbed into the Land-Rover. 'It's half past three, Carol,' said Mrs. Cameron settling herself behind the steering-wheel. 'Time we were on our way.'

Carol slipped in beside her and shut the door with a satisfied slam. 'It's been a wonderful day,' she said. 'Honestly, I don't think I've ever enjoyed myself so much.'

'I'm so glad,' replied Mrs. Cameron who had grown very fond of her assistant. 'It has been such fun to bring you, Carol, you're so interested and appreciative. I feel very unkind dragging you all the way home tonight – it is a long way and we shan't be back much before nine or ten o'clock. But I want to be home when the new ponies arrive . . .'

'My goodness, yes!' agreed Carol. 'I can't wait to see Mr. Cameron's face when he sees Jet. Anyway, I don't mind the long journey and it's all been well worth it.'

Mrs. Cameron checked that her new tack was all in and they drove slowly across the field. 'We will make straight north for the Queensferry,' she said. 'We should get a chance to stretch our legs when we are crossing and then we'll have a stop farther on about seven o'clock for dinner somewhere.'

They swung out of the park gates on to the road. Carol sighed happily and leant back in her seat. She wouldn't change this life with a job in London for anything. She thought about her friends from school, busy now with office jobs and probably having a gay time in the busy metropolis. Let them, she thought, I'm having just as good a time. She missed Hugh, she had to admit to herself and he would have loved the day at the sales. But he was still at school and that was a necessity they all had to go through.

Mrs. Cameron looked at her for a second and said quietly.

'Hugh would have enjoyed the day, wouldn't he, Carol?'

How ever had she guessed her thoughts? Carol nodded and smiled ruefully.

'He certainly would . . .' she agreed.

'Never mind, you'll see him at Christmas,' Mrs. Cameron reminded her. 'And then if you can stick us until Easter perhaps he will come and stay for some of his holidays?'

'Oh, he'd love that,' Carol replied. 'And don't you think that Swallow would be a perfect mount for him?'

Mrs. Cameron laughed. 'Indeed he would, Carol,' she agreed. 'That's a very good idea. But in the meantime I hope you will give him a bit of work.'

'Rather!'

'We're going to have quite a busy winter,' Mrs. Cameron told her. 'We've got the young ponies to school and the foals to handle and if we get bad weather all the animals need regular feeding. Then, in the snow, I expect you'd like to do a bit of ski-ing. I don't think you will be bored.'

'No, I'm sure I shan't,' Carol promised.

CHAPTER NINE

THE WINTER TRAINING
PERIOD

WITH the departure of the last of the guests in October the pony-trekking season closed and Carol settled down to enjoy the winter months. There was much work to be done. At the beginning of November the riding ponies were turned out on free range where they were able to roam for miles as their ancestors had done before them. They moved up and down the glen in small groups finding their food amongst the sweet grass which grew along the burnside and in areas where the heather was sparse. The constant ranging about kept them in good condition and it was delightful to watch them from the farmhouse and to pick out the individual ponies with the help of binoculars. The ponies were on free range for about two months until the bad weather necessitated bringing them down for supplementary feeding.

The young stock were moved from the field in which they had spent all summer. It was necessary with a large number of ponies to graze the pasture in strict rotation. Horses by their methods of grazing can ruin a pasture quicker than cattle or sheep. They eat very few weeds and would rather starve than feed on some of the coarse grasses. When a field has been grazed for a time exclusively by horses it begins to look patchy, with some areas quite untouched and other sweeter parts cropped right down so that in places the bare earth is exposed. On a farm, of course, this problem can easily be dealt with. The field can be rested, other stock can be grazed and the pasture kept in good condition by harrowing and by the use of fertilizers.

A prevalence of weeds is a sign of poor land. Docks, creeping thistles, nettles, bracken and buttercups are useless for feeding but buttercup and thistle can now be reduced by spraying before the flowering stage and bracken and docks can be almost eradicated by persistent cutting.

The foals were brought into a small paddock with their mothers just beside the farmhouse. In this way they would be constantly in sight and sound of human activities. Carol had several lessons from Mrs. Cameron about their handling and was then put in complete charge of them. The general idea during the first year of a pony's life is to handle it thoroughly and teach it the elements of manners. This could be done by anyone possessing horse sense and a quiet patient nature with animals. The foal halters were carefully adjusted and made of narrow leather. Once the animal had become used to having this slipped on and off it begins to wear it out in the field during the day. Of course it was very important that these halters were a good fit and did not chafe the foal. If it was too loose it could catch on fencing and give the youngster a nasty fright.

Each morning Carol had to catch the foals and bring them into the stableyard. She handled them quietly for a few minutes, running her hand down each leg and picking up the tiny hooves. She was not allowed to buckle a leading rein on to the halter but had to slip it through the back of the nose-band. When the leading lessons started Mrs. Cameron would lead the foal's mother in front and if the foal showed a tendency to be stubborn Carol would put her right hand around its rump and half lift it along.

It quickly got the idea of walking out properly on a leading rein. Later the foals loved their walks with Carol and they explored the farm and its inhabitants with great interest.

... Held firmly under the chin

By October, when Carol began daily work with them, the two foals at Croftmore were six months' old. She had to be very firm. They had quite overcome their fear of human beings and frequently tried to be rough and to get loose. When the foal began to jump about and toss its little head defiantly she held it firmly just under the chin and walked as close as possible against its shoulder. It was important not to let it break away from her, because once it achieved this, it realized its own strength and would play up each time it was taken out. If a reprimand was necessary she must never hit it across the nose but administer a sharp rap over the rump with a switch or the end of the lead rein.

After a few weeks she had to place a woollen wither pad on the foal's back. After a few days the pad was fastened on with a narrow webbed belly-band. The buckle of the roller had to be over the pad so that it could not catch on anything or irritate the foal. The pad and the roller were put on daily and left on for the duration of the walk. Carol suggested letting the foals loose in the field wearing their rollers so that they might become more quickly accustomed to them. But Mrs. Cameron discouraged this because she said the foals would gallop and might work the pad loose and get a fright when it fell off and the roller slipped round.

By the time they were yearlings they were expected to be easily led in hand, quiet to handle and groom and used to wearing the roller and pad for a reasonable length of time.

October was a lovely month for weather in the highlands and the few guests that visited the centre for riding enjoyed long fine days in the saddle. The mornings were very cold with a touch of frost but the days were wonderfully crisp and clear. Mrs. Cameron always regretted that more people did not visit them during this month because the weather was generally very reliable and there were fewer midges. July and August were often wet months in the highlands.

There were two young four-year-old ponies, Ladybird and Gipsy which Carol and Mrs. Cameron rode daily and they continued to do this all winter except when they were prevented by severe snow and frost. These ponies were fully broken but still had much to learn because they were to be used in the coming season for regular daily work by all types of visiting riders. The rides were a great delight and Carol learnt much from Mrs. Cameron's long experience with ponies. Carol grew to know and love the countryside around Croftmore and she was able to see a good deal of the abundant wild life of the area.

The ponies had to be taught to be obedient to the aids, to walk quietly for long stretches in single file without bunching or falling back. They had to learn that they must not continually snatch at the grass whenever the party paused. This was difficult to curb completely and some ponies were greedier than others, but it was necessary to attempt to control the annoying habit because a beginner could find it very tiresome. The ponies were also taught to stand quietly when mounted and dismounted and during all handling and grooming. So many visitors to the trekking centre were quite inexperienced and it was necessary to ensure that the ponies provided for their enjoyment were as quiet and well behaved as possible.

One of the ponies, Ladybird, showed a marked distaste for crossing water and as there were frequent burns in the area to be forded this tendency had to be overcome. Most young ponies dislike entering water but with a little patience they can quickly be taught. Mrs. Cameron would take the nervous pony and Carol would ride into the water in front to encourage it. It paused on the river's edge and blew at the water, pawed the ground and refused to enter without persistent encouragement. Carol, waiting in the middle of the ford with her pony, had to keep its head held up and alert, so that it did not get ideas about lying down. To begin with the lesson took about twenty minutes before the pony would enter the river and after it had been persuaded to do so, they rode back and forth across the ford so that the pony became accustomed to the swirl and rush of the clear cool water around its legs.

This lesson was repeated daily with great patience and perseverance and quite soon Ladybird began to follow his companion in quite easily. The day he began to paw the water Mrs. Cameron pronounced the lesson completely learnt.

'He is getting bored with the water now and has quite stopped being afraid of it,' she said to Carol. 'We shan't worry about coming down here for any further lessons.'

'They are very intelligent ponies,' remarked Carol. 'He hasn't taken very long to learn.'

'Yes, they learn quickly but you have to be firm with them too,' she replied. 'They can pick up bad habits very quickly and will take advantage of novice riders if they are not well schooled when they are young.'

One evening they had been out riding the two young ponies after tea. It was cool and pleasant and the midges were not the nuisance that they were during the height of the summer at this time of day. They rode out of the forest and came in sight of the farm some hundred yards ahead of them across the heather.

Suddenly Mrs. Cameron reined in her pony. Then she pointed ahead without speaking and Carol saw at once what she had seen. A deer was standing only a short distance in front of them. It had not seen them or caught a whiff of their wind, and it stood looking up towards the farm. It was quite small and incredibly dainty and Carol could see that it had two little pointed horns on its head. As they watched, another deer suddenly appeared from behind a rock, wandering quite undisturbed towards its mate, with head down nibbling at the short grass among the heather clumps.

They kept motionless for a second or two observing the

two deer who remained momentarily still, unaware of their presence. The ponies cocked their ears and watched too. Then the one in front saw them. Perhaps he caught their wind or the sound of one of the ponies shifting a hindleg. Instantly, the other one was on the alert. The large dark eyes stared at them for a second and then in a flash they were off, the leader bounding away over the heather closely followed by his wife. Their slim legs carried them swiftly over the rough ground and they were quickly swallowed up in the wood.

'Roe deer!' said Mrs. Cameron. 'There are lots about here now. They get much bolder when the really cold weather comes.'

'One of them had little horns,' said Carol. 'But the other one didn't.'

'A buck and a doe,' Mrs. Cameron replied. 'They frequently move in pairs. In the spring I expect you will see a fawn too. They are the daintiest little creatures.'

When they rode into the farmyard Mr. Cameron had just returned from inspecting his sheep on the hill. He had been out all the afternoon and Jet's dark coat was streaked with sweat. His collie dog lay in the yard, his hindlegs stretched straight out behind in a characteristic attitude of the breed and his tongue lolled pink and dripping from his mouth.

'Where have you been?' inquired his wife, noticing the exhausted dog.

'We were a long way out,' replied her husband leading the black pony into his stall. 'I've never known the sheep so far out for late October. Floss had a long way to travel to round them up for me but we found them all. I must be bringing them down soon in case we get a snowstorm next month.' He stripped Jet's saddle from the pony's damp back. 'You need a rub down, my lad. I had to hurry home for milking because Jock is off this afternoon.'

'I'll rub him down for you, Mr. Cameron,' said Carol. 'Tell me what feed he gets and I'll look after him.'

'Two handfuls of oats and the same of bran,' he told her, 'and fill his hay net up too. Thank you, Carol, I'll leave him to you ...'

He hurried away with his dog at heel to fetch the two house cows for milking. He had been a little apprehensive about the Fell pony when it first arrived, but was soon as delighted with it as with his familiar Highland ponies.

That year the snow came early. One morning towards the end of November Carol awoke and drawing back the window curtains saw through the dusk that big flakes of snow were drifting gently down. She stood for a few minutes until her eyes grew accustomed to the semi-dark, marvelling at the changed world. There had been a good covering of snow during the night. She shivered and then got quickly back into bed.

During the morning they carried wooden hay racks down to the ponies' fields. The ponies, which had been turned out on the hill after the close of the season, were down now at the foot of the glen. The unexpected snowfall had covered their natural sustenance and they were grouped dejectedly looking up towards the farm.

'We should have had them down a few days ago,' said Mrs. Cameron. 'This snow has taken us by surprise. Bring two halters, Carol, and we'll go straight up and catch two of them and the rest will follow. Angus says we can put them in the burn field.'

They walked down to the ponies, keeping to the cart-track where the marks of the tractor had been before them. It was pleasant to walk through the snow, to feel it crunch and to leave footsteps across virgin territory. Soon the farm road would be a mass of tracks of boots and tyres and the snow would turn to mud and slush. They brought the ponies up into their field and filled their hay racks with golden sweet-smelling hay. The ponies ate hungrily, pulling the wisps of hay out of the racks greedily and laying back their ears at their companions. The two racks had been placed well apart and away from the edge of the field so that the ponies could stand all round each of them. Otherwise, the nervous animals were intimidated by the bullies.

'Why not just spread the hay out on the ground?' asked Carol.

'If we did that, it would get trampled on,' explained Mrs. Cameron. 'And, worse still, it would blow all over the field in a wind. I think good hay racks are essential and every trekking centre should have them. They are not expensive or difficult to have made.'

Carol was thrusting hay into the racks.

'Shake it out well,' called Mrs. Cameron. She had moved away to examine a pony's hoof. 'Never put tightly packed hay in a rack or net. Come up mare!' She was examining Jean's hoof and the pony was impatient for her hay. 'We must get the blacksmith again soon to file these hooves down. We don't want any broken feet.' She released the mare and watched her find a vacant place near one of the hay racks and begin to pull at the fodder.

Carol had finished dispensing the hay and came across to stand beside Mrs. Cameron and watch the ponies feed.

'How often do you need to file their feet down in winter?' she asked. 'You had all their shoes taken off at the end of the season only six or seven weeks ago. I thought native ponies had hard feet which didn't need much attention.'

'You're quite right they don't,' agreed Mrs. Cameron. 'The majority of these Highland ponies won't need attention until the spring. But Jean is different and I have to watch her feet closely. Before I bought her she was with a family in Berwickshire. They have very good pasture there and during the summer when the children were at school they turned her out in a big field and left her there for two months. Of course, there was far too much grass for one pony and it was a while before anyone noticed she was lying down a lot. When her owner finally went down to see her, he found she could barely stand. The rich unrestricted pasture had affected her feet and she had developed laminitis.'

'What's laminitis?' Carol had never heard the word before.

'It is a fever in the feet. It's a dreadful disease for a pony and very common, particularly amongst small ponies. Horses are susceptible too.'

'And it is caused by too much food?'

'Yes, entirely. It is fatal to turn a pony out on rich land and forget about it. Some animals are all right but the trouble is that once affected, although it can be temporarily cured, it will recur immediately if the pony is overfed and under exercised.'

'What did they do to cure Jean, if she could hardly walk?'

Mrs. Cameron sighed. 'She must have been a sorry sight. I've known ponies so badly affected that they had to be destroyed. You have to be cruel to be kind and the pony must be half-starved and the feet cut back to help it. A good blacksmith knows how to cut out the affected part. In time it will come right and the pony can be used again. Jean is quite sound now; in fact, as you know, she is one of our best ponies, but I have to watch her all the year round. This hill land is ideal, of course, and we have never had a case of laminitis, but the native ponies are susceptible to it if they are allowed free range on rich grass.'

It was starting to snow again and now that the ponies were all fed, they began to walk back up to the farm.

'Tomorrow you can go down with the tractor,' said Mrs. Cameron. 'It will take several trusses of hay and you can fill up the tracks in the two fields. If the snow continues for a few days we shall start extra feeding with mashes and pony cubes.'

'Do look at the foals!' exclaimed Carol. The two young colts were playing in the snow, nuzzling the strange cold white stuff for an instant and then tossing up their heads and cantering round in astonished and delighted circles. 'Of course, they've never seen snow before, have they?'

'No, indeed, they haven't,' agreed Mrs. Cameron. 'And I expect they are hungry too. We must feed them some concentrates, and their mothers too.'

'Oughtn't we to bring them into the stables while the snow lasts?'

'Oh no, it isn't necessary,' Mrs. Cameron assured Carol. 'They have a shed for shelter. These native pony foals are very hardy and it wouldn't do to spoil them now. They will have to get used to wintering outside. Anyway, as you can see, they love the snow.'

The snow continued into December and Carol was able to try her skill at ski-ing. It was possible to hire all the necessary equipment in Aviemore and she had a lot of fun with the many young people who visited the Cairngorms at week-ends. At Christmas she was to return home for a holiday and Mrs. Cameron told her to stay away for a week or two and enjoy herself.

'There is nothing to hurry back for here and you haven't seen your family for nearly six months,' she said. 'Take two weeks' holiday now, and when you come back I am going to pay you a small working wage of thirty shillings.'

'Am I really experienced enough to be paid?' Carol asked.

'Well, in the pony-trekking business as in everything to do with horses there is still much for you to learn,' Mrs, Cameron replied. 'But you have worked very hard. Carol, and are proving yourself most useful to me. I think you deserve to start on a small wage.'

Carol felt very thrilled at the news. It would help to console her parents when she told them that she intended to return to Croftmore for at least another trekking season.

When she returned to London she found to her relief that the family had been expecting her to continue her job with ponies. It was her first evening home and it was lovely to relax in the old rocking-chair before the fire and feel that a whole delicious fortnight stretched ahead with nothing to do but laze about and shop and see her friends.

'We knew you were enjoying yourself from your letters,' her mother told her, 'and Hugh came back so enthusiastic about everything after his holiday. He said he was certain you would stay for the winter.'

'Longer than just the winter, I hope,' interrupted Hugh. 'I thought you said I could go up for two weeks in the Easter holidays.'

'Yes, darling, I did, and although we shall miss you it will be fun for Carol to have you with her,' replied his mother. 'If you are still there in the summer, Carol, then Daddy and I will have to make a trip up to visit you. Goodness knows what Granny will say when we pass her by; she says she wishes you would get a job at a pony-trekking centre in Northumberland.'

'Well I can't, because there are only a few at the moment in Northumberland,' Carol replied. 'And none large enough to take a pupil. But, Mummy, why don't you bring Granny up with you. She would love a trip to Scotland?'

'Yes, I think perhaps she would,' agreed Mrs. Spencer. 'Anyway, it's a long way ahead and maybe you will be sick of ponies by then . . .'

Carol and Hugh exchanged glances.

'You sound hopeful, Mum,' Hugh teased her. 'But I shouldn't count on it if I were you!'

CHAPTER TEN

PREPARATION FOR ANOTHER SEASON

IT was a long hard winter and the snow lay on the farm until early March. It would lie on the high tops of the Cairngorms for many weeks longer. The ponies had grown thick shaggy coats and took little exercise in the frost and snow, occasionally scratching at the unyielding ground with their hooves to uncover the grass underneath. Most of the time they stood grouped about the gate, well-fed and lazy. There was no need to scratch for a living. When the thaw came and the grass began to show again, they moved away and began to crop at the short stunted growth.

'We must begin riding again, Carol,' said Mrs. Cameron as they went down to feed the ponies one morning in early March. 'They will all be very unfit with doing nothing for the last two months. The frost is coming out of the ground now and we should be able to get out by ten o'clock each day. It will be interesting to see how Swallow shapes...'

'Yes, I'm longing to try him,' said Carol. 'And we must take out Ladybird and Gipsy and make sure that Ladybird hasn't forgotten his lessons with the river. How soon do the first guests arrive?'

'Not until the second week in April. I have four adults and two children booked for a week. Then we have a full house for Easter. I think we shall need to use every pony we can. We have several visitors coming over daily during the week-end from other hotels in the district.'

'It is just as well Hugh isn't coming until after Easter,' Carol replied. 'Daddy said he thought you would have all the good ponies booked.'

'Well, it will be much nicer for him to come when we aren't so busy, I think he had Jean last season.'

'Yes he did, but this time we were going to let him try Swallow,' Carol reminded her.

'Of course we were,' agreed Mrs. Cameron. 'He should suit Hugh very well. You are used to the ponies now, Carol and quite responsible, so this season I can let you and Hugh go out alone occasionally. Of course most of the time I shall need your help with the guests on trek but there will be a few afternoons or evenings when you can go out by yourselves.'

'Oh, thank you, that will be fun!'

'Our visitors have started booking earlier than ever this season. I had several letters in January booking for peak periods and we have quite a number of foreigners.' Mrs. Cameron finished shaking out the hay and began to pack it into one of the hay racks. 'So the ponies are doing their bit to attract the tourists to Scotland!'

'Gosh, overseas visitors!' exclaimed Carol. 'I shall certainly get experience of dealing with every kind of client.'

'That's very important,' replied Mrs. Cameron. 'One day you may have a trekking centre of your own or you might get a job managing one for a hotel. There is a good opening now for operators in this field. Pony trekking means an attractive feature on a hotel brochure and seems to appeal to holiday-makers who like country districts and pursuits. Of course you needn't limit yourself to Scotland—'

K

'Oh, but I love it up here,' interrupted Carol.

'I know you do,' agreed Mrs. Cameron. 'But when it comes to work you have to go where a good job offers. You might get the chance to go abroad – trekking has caught on in Iceland and Holland and several other countries. Get about while you are young, Carol. Once you marry and settle down the opportunity doesn't arise so easily again. Not every girl marries a tycoon, you know!'

Carol laughed. 'I suppose you are right. Anyway, at the moment I'm quite happy in England, or Scotland, but I'll certainly remember what you said about trekking abroad. It sounds a splendid idea.'

They began walking back to the farm. 'What about the examiner who inspects your centre. Will you have to be inspected this year?'

'Oh yes, of course, we like to have a Certificate of Approval for each current season,' Mrs. Cameron replied. 'The representative for the Ponies of Britain Club is due this month. I expect many of the trekking centres in England are inspected much earlier in the winter so that they can advertise their certificate for the following season.'

'I shall be interested to see what he inspects,' said Carol.

'Everything,' replied Mrs. Cameron. 'You may go round with him and you should learn a lot. He goes over each pony and all the saddlery most thoroughly. I expect in some centres the premises need careful investigation too. I look forward to his annual visit and he can be very helpful. I have one pony I would like to sell to another trekking centre and he may be useful over that.'

Carol nodded. 'He must visit quite a number of trekking centres. But it isn't compulsory for your establishment to be awarded a certificate, is it?'

'No, but more and more operators are appreciating the wisdom of being officially approved. Nevertheless, there will always be some who don't. All we can do is to try to educate the riding public to visit the establishments which carry certificates. This should be achieved in time, but I dare say there will always be people who are ignorant of anything to do with horses and riding who have to learn through bitter experience.'

The expected visit of the Ponies of Britain Club representative took place a week later. It was a wet day but the inspector was not deterred by the elements. With Carol at his elbow to assist with holding the ponies and showing him all the equipment, he looked everything over with great thoroughness and care. The ponies had all been stabled for the visit and they spent all morning in the buildings. The rain poured down in sheets turning the yard into a quagmire and the hills were obliterated by mist and cloud.

'This doesn't seem a very cheerful spot!' joked the inspector putting his head out of the stable door and looking ruefully at the gloomy outlook.

'Oh, but it is really,' Carol assured him, slipping a halter on one of the ponies and turning it round to be inspected. 'The view is glorious—'

'When you can see it,' he replied.

'Well, you nearly always can,' she promised him. 'Honestly, it doesn't rain like this very often. It's really a beautiful part of the country and simply perfect for pony trekking.'

'Oh, yes, I had heard it was,' he assured her, running an expert eye over the pony she was holding. 'You seem to have fallen in love with it anyway. I'm only sorry that I have chosen a wet day to come here.' He ran his hand down the pony's forelegs and paused whilst he felt behind one of its knees. 'This pony has had a splint at some time.

But his legs seem sound enough now. Let's take a look at his teeth,' he drew back the pony's lips and looked critically at his teeth. 'He is quite young, not more than seven or eight years, I should say.'

At the end of the day Carol had learnt a great deal. Towards the end of his visit she plied the inspector with questions, and seeing that she was genuinely keen and interested he gave her as much information as she wanted. He told her that there was a Rally of pony-trekking operators and instructors being held near Edinburgh the following month and advised her to try and go.

'That's a very good idea, Carol,' agreed Mrs. Cameron. By this time they were all enjoying a cup of tea in the guests' lounge. 'I had forgotten about it because I don't think Angus or I can go this year.'

'But I'm not an operator or an instructor!' protested Carol.

'That doesn't matter,' the inspector assured her. 'The idea of the Rally is for people like you, who want to become pony-trekking groom instructors and operators, to have an opportunity to meet others with similar interests. What is more, all prospective instructors are members of the Advisory Committee on pony trekking graded by to the Scottish Council of Physical Recreation.'

'That sounds wonderful,' said Carol. 'But I don't really think I am experienced enough yet, and if Mrs. Cameron will have me I want to stay here another year. I love the country and the ponies and I'm sure I couldn't go anywhere better for training . . .'

'Of course we will have you, Carol,' Mrs. Cameron promised her. She reached for the teapot and filled the inspector's cup. 'You've been a great help to me and I shall miss you when you do go. But I'm inclined to agree with you about attending the Rally. In another year's time you would benefit much more from it and by then you may be looking seriously for a job. It is really a splendid opportunity of meeting the organizers of Scottish pony-trekking and riding holiday centres.'

'It will be something to look forward to and to save towards,' said Carol. 'Is it expensive?'

'No, not at all,' replied the inspector. 'It is usually held at a good hotel and the fees include all board and lodging. It costs about five pounds and I believe they charge ten shillings extra per trek. There are practical demonstrations, discussions, generally a Brains Trust one evening and a Film Show.' He stood up and handed his cup to Mrs. Cameron. 'Now I really must leave you all, I've a long way to drive this evening. I'm due at a trekking centre south of Perth early tomorrow morning. I have very much enjoyed meeting you and inspecting your admirable establishment.'

They walked out to the yard where he had left his car. It had stopped raining now and the clouds had lifted a little so that only the tops of the hills were obscured. A watery sun was beginning to break through. 'It looks as though I'm going to get a fine evening for my drive. Good-bye, Carol, and good luck, and don't forget to book in plenty of time for next year's Spring Rally!'

'Indeed, I won't forget,' she promised him, 'and I hope you will find me still here when you come again next March.'

After this visit the days passed quickly and soon the first guests of the season had arrived. The days grew longer and lighter and the weather warmer. Spring was in the air and the woods were full of birds and the grass began to turn greener and the trees to burst into leaf. The highlands were very beautiful and Carol's days were full. When Hugh arrived after Easter the days had settled down into a full routine of work and Carol had many responsibilities. She was not yet allowed to lead a trek on her own but there were days when she and her brother were able to enjoy an hour or two rambling in the heather on two of the ponies.

They were in the little harness-room cleaning tack after tea one evening. Hugh swished his sponge down the reins of his pony's bridle and then dried them briskly with a chamois leather. Carol was polishing a snaffle bit.

'You seem to be settled up here, Carol,' said Hugh. 'How long do you think you will stay?'

'Well, I think another year,' she replied, giving the bit a final rub and reaching for the headpiece of the bridle. 'Mrs. Cameron said I should be able to lead a few treks by August so long as the riders were not complete beginners. I love it here, Hugh. I'm doing work I enjoy, meeting new and interesting people every week and I'm out in the open air nearly all day.'

'It's ideal for you,' agreed Hugh. 'You always did love animals and the country.'

'Perhaps all the years in London make me appreciate the beautiful scenery here all the more.' Carol was buckling the newly polished bit back on to its bridle. 'I'm getting a small wage too and I should get more when I get another job. Or if I want to stay and work on here next season Mrs. Cameron will give me a rise. There, that's the last thing clean; are you finished yours, Hugh?'

'Jolly nearly.' He looped up the newly soaped reins and fastened them into the throat lash. 'There we are, now we can go and put the ponies out.' He followed his sister out of the little room.

The ponies nickered in anticipation. They always enjoyed going out for the night after a hard day's work. They had a long cool drink from the burn and a delicious roll in the grass.

. . . Roll in the grass

Carol led the black Fell pony and one of the Highland ponies out into the yard. As she waited for Hugh to join her with two more, she put her arm around Jet's strong neck. He lowered his head and blew gently into her hand. She stroked his thick tumbled mane and thought how content she was amongst these grand ponies. Pony trekking had certainly turned out to be the right life for her.

1963 REVISED LIST OF TREKKING AND RIDING HOLIDAY CENTRES AWARDED 'PONIES OF BRITAIN' CERTIFICATES OF APPROVAL

T. Trekking Holidays; R. Residential; N.R. Non-Residential; R.H. Riding Holidays; A.H. Attached to Hotel; C. Caravan to let; N.H. & G.H. Near-by Hotels and Guest Houses; F. Farmhouse; Ct. Cottage; H. Hostel.

ENGLAND

Beds.	R.H.	Lilley Riding Stables, Lilley, Nr. Luton.	N.R.
Berks.	R.H.	Cadogan Riding School, Holyport, Maidenhead (Under Royal patronage)	R.
	R.H.	Morley's Riding Stables, Titness Park, Sunninghill.	N.H.
	R.H.	Cross Lanes Riding Centre, Reading Road, Arborfield. (Instructional and Working Pupils)	R. & daily
Cheshire	R.H.	Black Horse Riding School, Rectory Road, West Kirby, Wirral.	N.H. & G.H.
	R.H.	Keele Riding and Livery Stables, Madeley Heath Farm, Madeley Heath, Nr. Crewe.	N.H. & G.H.
	R.H.	The Altrincham and District Residential Riding Academy, Stonedelph Farm, Millington, Nr. Altrincham	R. A.H.
Cumberland	T. & R.H.	Thornthwaite Hall, Thornthwaite, Keswick.	N.H. & G.H.
	R.	Scotby School of Equitation, Scotby, Nr. Carlisle.	R.
	T.	(From Elterwater Farm and Eskdale for Hotels.)	N.H.
Devon	T.	Holne Park and Hawson Riding Stables, Buckfastleigh. (NO NOVICES – Teenagers and children preferred.)	R. N.H. & G.H.
	R.H.	Corscombe Riding School, Okehampton.	N.H. & G.H.
	T.	Blackcock Hotel, Molland Station.	A.H.
	R.H.	Mrs. C. Case, The Forge, Holne, Newton Abbot. (Unaccompanied children taken.)	R.
	T. & R.H.	Gidleigh Trekking Centre, Gidleigh, Nr. Chagford.	R. (4 only)
	R.H.	Ring of Bells, North Bovey, Newton Abbot. (EXPERIENCED RIDERS ONLY.)	R.

ENGLAND—*cont.*

T. & R.H.	Sherberton Pony Stud, Princetown	N.H. & G.H.
T.	Shilstone Rocks Pony Stud, Widecombe-in-the-Moor	R.
T.	Gidleigh Park Hotel Riding Stables, Chagford.	A.H.
Dorset		
R.H.	Mrs. Ellis, Bailie Leaze, Sturminster Marshall, Wimborne. (CHILDREN ONLY.)	R.
Essex		
R.H.	Ardleigh Park, Nr. Colchester. (15 YEARS AND UNDER – CHILDREN A SPECIALITY).	R.
Hants.		
R.H.	Barton School of Equitation, New Barton Farm, Lower Chilcombe, Winchester	N.R.
R.H.	Broadlands, Medstead, Hants. (CHILDREN 16 YEARS AND UNDER ONLY) including Christmas and Easter.)	R.
R.H.	Compton Arms Stables, Stoney Cross, Nr. Lyndhurst.	R. N.H. & G.H.
T. & R.H.	Lyndhurst Riding School, Lyndhurst.	N.H. & G.H.
R.H.	Harroway House Riding School, Penton, Andover. (CHILDREN A SPECIALITY. 15 YEARS AND UNDER.)	R.
Hants	Stocklands, Petersfield. (Instructional.)	
R.H.		R. N.H.
Hunts.	Allerton Equitation School, Moat House, Alconbury Hill.	
R.H.		R.
Lancs.	Sunfield Riding School, Turf Pit Lane, Moorside, Oldham.	
R.H.		N.R.
T.	Goat Gap Farm, Clapham, Lancaster.	R. (4 only) N.H.
T. & R.H.	Mrs. C. M. McNally, 25 Stoney Bank Road, Earby, Via Colne.	N.H.
Northants.		
R.H.	Miss M. Ward Hunt, The Manor House, Wadenhoe, Nr. Oundle, Peterborough.	N.H. & G.H.
Northumberland		
T.	Miss Jean Girling, Wreigh Close, Thropton, Morpeth.	N.R., N.H. & G.H.
Shropshire		
T.	Malthouse Stables, Little Stretton.	R.
Somerset		
T. & R.H.	Dunster Riding Stables, Dunster.	R. N.H.
T. & R.H.	Lorna Doone Hotel, Porlock. (NO TEENAGERS – NO BEGINNERS.)	A.H.
R.H.	Exmoor and Metropole Stables, North Road, Minehead.	N.H. & G.H.
T.	Exmoor and Metropole Stables. Apply to: Rem-U-Era Hotel, Northfield Road, Minehead.	R.

Surrey	R.H.	Porlock Vale Riding School, Porlock.	R.
	R.H.	Scot's Stables, Nether Stowey, Nr. Bridgwater.	N.H. & G.H.
	R.H.	Bridge Barn Riding School, Arthurs Bridge, Woking.	N.H. & G.H.
	R.H.	Lockner Farm Riding School, Chilworth, Guildford.	R.F.
	R.H.	Woodcote Riding Centre, Chalk Lane, Epsom.	N.R. N.H.
Sussex	R.H.	Bryckden Riding School, Waldron, Heathfield. (CHILDREN ONLY.)	R.
Warwicks.	R.H.	Darley Mill School of Equitation, Kingswood Farm, Lapworth.	N.R.
Westmorland	R.H.	Tarn Hows Hotel, Hawkshead, Ambleside.	A.H.
Yorks.	T. & R.H.	Rupin Riding School, Heath Hill Farm, Mount Tabor, Halifax.	N.H. & G.H.
	T. & R.H.	Wharfedale Riding School and Trekking Centre, Menston-in-Wharfedale, Ilkley.	N.R.

SCOTLAND

Aberdeen	T. & R.H.	Annesley Riding School, Annesley, Torphins.	R. & Ct.
	T.	James Archibald, 2 Richmond Place, Ballater. Apply to: Scottish Youth Hostels Assoc., Edinburgh.	Youth Hostel.
	R.H.	John G. Taylor, Riding Stables, Birch Cottage, Dyce. (Especially children.)	N.R., N.H., G.H.
Angus	T.	Glenesk Pony Trekking Centre, Dalbreck, Tarfside, Brechin.	F.
Argyll	T. & R.H.	The Misses I. & I.J. MacIntosh, Inverinan Lodge, by Taynuilt.	R.
	T.	Succoth Farm, Strachur. (Mr. Donald Campbell.)	N.H.
Isle of Arran	T.	Cairn House, Blackwaterfoot.	R.
Inverness	R.H.	Miss Georgie Henschel, Altnacriche, Aviemore.	R.
	T.	Inchnacardo Hotel, Fort Augustus.	A.H.
	T.	Borlum Farm Guest House, Drummadrochit.	R. N.H., G.H.
Kinross-shire	R.H.	Fossoway Riding Centre, Tullibole Mill, Crook of Devon.	R.
Lanarks.	T.	Toftcombs Hotel, Biggar.	A.H.
Morayshire	T.	Rothes Glen Hotel, Rothes.	A.H.
	T. & R.H.	Forres Pony Trekking and Riding Centre, 'Craigellochie', Burdshaugh, Forres	N.R. N.H. & G.H.

SCOTLAND—cot.

Perthshire	T. & R.H.	Hugh McGregor at Castle Hotel, Glendevon.	A.H.
	T.	Hugh McGregor at Covenanter's Inn, Aberfoyle.	A.H.
	T.	Hugh McGregor at the Trossachs Hotel.	A.H.
	T.	Killiecrankie Hotel, Killiecrankie.	A.H.
	T.	Spital of Glenshee Hotel, by Blairgowrie.	A.H.
	T.	Tilt Hotel, Blair Atholl.	A.H.
	T. & R.H.	Pan School of Equitation, Dam of Quoigs, Greenloaning, Dunblane.	N.H. & G.H.
Ross-shire	T.	Mrs. Mackay-Scobie, Rhidorroch, Ullapool.	N.H. & G.H., C.,Ct
Roxburgh.	T.	The King's Arms Hotel, Melrose.	A.H.
Sutherland	T.	Caledonian Hotel, Bonar Bridge.	A.H.

WALES

Brecon	T. & R.H.	Crickhowell Riding Club, Crickhowell.	R.
		(NO TEENAGERS UNATTENDED.)	
	T. & R.H.	Duhonw Riding School and Pony Trekking Assoc. Builth Wells.	N.H. & G.H.
Cardigan	T.	Tregaron Pony Trekking Assoc., Castle House, Tregaron.	N.H. & G.H.
ICELAND	T.	Iceland Tourist Information Bureau, 161 Piccadilly, W.1.	A.H. H.H.

FURTHER PARTICULARS AND BROCHURES CAN BE OBTAINED FROM THE 'PONIES OF BRITAIN', BROOKSIDE FARM, ASCOT, BERKSHIRE, ON RECEIPT OF A STAMPED ADDRESSED ENVELOPE.

INDEX